€2

ROSENHEIM &
WINDERMERE

By the same author:

The Jerusalem Guide, 1973
Cork, with Eiléan Ní Chuilleanáin, 1977
Dublin Ninety Drawings,1981
Voices from Stones with Myrna Haugaard, 1983
Dublin Bay,1989
West of West,1990
Dublin Drawn and Quartered, 1991
Ultimate Dublin,1991
Blue Guide Ireland, 1995
Archaeology and Biblical Interpretation (contributor) 1997
Dublin and Ireland, 1997
The Laugh of Lost Men, 1997
The Irish Round Tower, 1999
The Ballad of Reading Gaol, woodcuts (Oscar Wilde), 1999
Blue Guide Dublin, 2001
The Encyclopaedia of Ireland, General Editor, 2003
Librarians, Poets and Scholars (contributor) 2007
I am of Ireland, editor, 2010
Ink-Stained Hands, 2011
Island of Shadow, editor, 2011

Print portfolios:

The Jerusalem Portfolio, 1973
Kilkenny City and Topography, 1982
The Myth of Icarus, 1988
The Ballad of Reading Gaol, 1998

ROSENHEIM & WINDERMERE

BRIAN LALOR

SOMERVILLE PRESS

Somerville Press,
Dromore, Bantry,
Co. Cork, Ireland

First published 2011

Designed by Jane Stark
seamistgraphics@gmail.com

Typeset in Adobe Garamond Pro
Title in Gill Sans

ISBN: 978-0-9562231-6-6

Printed and bound by GraphyCems,
Villatuerta, Navarra, Spain

For Poppy Pohlmann,
blooming under a different sky.

The tumult and the shouting dies;
The Captains and the Kings depart:

Rudyard Kipling, 'Recessional' (1897)

CHAPTER 1

Grandmother lay like a jaded odalisque, dying throughout the entirety of my childhood. I sat in the window of her darkened bedroom where I had been sent by my parents to keep her company. My elder brother had previously been drafted into this role but had failed the test. He fidgeted. Although at an early age he could fluently read books or the newspaper aloud, negotiating the most unfamiliar vocabulary and nomenclature with ease and speed, this considerable social asset when visiting the ill or bedridden was considered subservient to the fault of fidgeting. I, on the contrary, who could not read with any fluency even to myself, was not a fidgeter and therefore more acceptable as a sickroom companion. During one of a number of local epidemics, I had contracted polio and had not been sent to school. On the days when I was not at home in Windermere to receive physiotherapy, massage or, like an unemployed Shirley Temple, was just resting, I was free to be made use of as a token carer and flag-bearer of family concern.

Some months earlier, before my illness had been detected, my mother and I were proceeding up the street on our way to the post office, she talking as I dawdled, dragging a foot through leaves in the gutter. My father, looking out through a side window of the house, noticed something alarming – I was visibly limping. Before we reached the main road, he had joined us and spoken inaudibly to my mother. Without further conversation, we turned back towards the house, my father holding my hand and observing the way I was walking. When we arrived at the house, I was sent under protest to go and lie down in my room, and shortly afterwards the doctor arrived. It was a hot summer's day and I wanted to be outside; I felt as though I was being punished for some unspecified crime. The doctor, who usually chatted in a 'hearty voice for children' manner, was strangely silent as he poked and prodded my legs, bidding me to walk across the room an unreasonable number of times, then leaving, to talk outside the door with my parents. Clearly something was going on and I was not being told.

When my brother returned from school, he was given a similar intense going-over, then put in a separate room. I had heard of bubonic plague, yellow fever, tuberculosis, and fancied myself to be dying in some style, although I felt perfectly well and resented the enforced incarceration. The muttering outside my bedroom door was making me anxious and I began to call out for attention. Used to my mother's perpetual apprehensions concerning her children's health, even when I had merely grazed my knee, I became alarmed because my normally more optimistic father also had a concerned expression that implied something was actually wrong. Perhaps I was going to die after all? Days passed and I remained imprisoned, with meals brought on trays, a concession granted only to Grandmother and the genuinely ill, yet still nothing was said, my questions evoking no response. Until tests confirmed that I had polio, the word was not uttered in my hearing, and then only in such hushed tones as to confirm my already aroused suspicions of imminent death. The public panic in Cork, caused by an epidemic of what was during the nineteen-forties regarded as an incurable and crippling condition, caused the infection to be treated as a major catastrophe. However, I had not been seriously affected and did not require hospital care, just lengthy periods of rest and the avoidance of any rough schoolyard activity. So I remained at home or at Grandmother's, left very much to my own devices.

In the mornings I was brought to Rosenheim, my maternal grandmother's house, by one or other of my parents or by Annie our maid, and was collected from there in the evenings. The day was my own, to while away as I pleased, between spending time with Grandmother or wandering as she slept. On being deposited, I was admonished to 'behave', a concept that was forever shifting, depending on the admonisher. From my mother, the word implied dutiful attendance at the bedside, from my father (accompanying it with a wink), the message was 'don't get up to mischief'. Annie's words were couched in a tone of hopeful though ill-founded optimism. 'Behave yourself now, or they will be complaining to your mother, an' I will be blempt for not controlling you.' I promised faithfully, more out of politeness and a desire to please Annie, of whom I was very fond, than from any conviction that I might be good. Without ever wishing to be uncooperative, I seemed to have a natural knack for doing things regarded by the adult world as reprehensible and as evidence of an awkward nature.

I sat in the window and looked out into the quiet street of tall, handsome redbrick houses with their well-tended gardens and firmly curtained windows, each with its lace-fringed blinds at the halfway position, the tassel hanging down below like the pendulum of the cuckoo clock. Every house was guarded from the street by its bastion of spiked railings and you would know which gate was being opened without even looking out the window, their screeches and rusty creaks were as individual as human voices: some gates cried out in anguish, others stuttered, one whinged loudly, a few were left swinging in the breeze and, to Grandmother's irritation, gossiped incessantly. I was curious about anything that moved on the street and would take note of any familiar or strange adult, child or dog, delivery-man or street-hawker as they passed. Later, I would describe them in the kitchen to Mrs Luby, the housekeeper, and ask about them.

Grandmother's bedroom, like the rest of the house, was enveloped in a darkness maintained by successive rows of curtains on the window, and by the universally dark colour and texture of the furniture, walls and carpets. My grandparents had moved into Rosenheim in the early nineteen hundreds and furnishings accumulated over half a century had come to occupy all spaces. Ponderous furniture, dark winking mirrors, and the (to me) extraordinary wall surfaces, covered with William Morris floral wallpaper which bore the bloom of half a century of smoky fires, were a source of constant wonder. Sometimes I stood so close to the wallpaper, I became dizzy as I attempted to follow its swirling designs.

When I became bored with looking into the street, and if Grandmother seemed to be sleeping soundly, I could investigate the vast number of drawers and cupboards in the room, escape to the rest of the house and explore, or go to the kitchen and chatter. My own home, only a few streets away from Rosenheim, a five-minute walk, seemed to fade in my mind the moment I entered the more heightened realities of my grandmother's. The periods that I spent at Rosenheim might have been just isolated days or they could extend into weeks. The reasons for these altered arrangements were never explained.

Beside Grandmother's bed, on a baize-covered table, was an accumulation of small brass hand-bells, graduated by size and timbre according to mood and necessity. Almost all the bells were in the form of miniature human figures, moulded by use and brass polish to smooth-surfaced ghosts of their original, more bright-cut selves: a seventeenth-century woman in a long gown with her hair in a tight bun, an eighteenth-century crinoline lady, one Dutch boy in clogs, and another Amsterdammer in voluminous baggy trousers. Some were more conventionally bell-shaped, and one, my favourite, was not lifted off the soft green surface of the side table, but was rung by tapping the little button on its top (it was probably a dinner table bell from an earlier age of domestic order, with bobbing housemaids in starched aprons and trailing bands). The bells were rung when Grandmother wished for attention, the crinoline lady if she was merely in need of distraction, the Dutch boys or the conventional bells if she wanted something, the push bell when she was agitated or feeling neglected. Sometimes she would ring them in succession and over an extended period, gradually raising the volume of the ringing until the urgent pounding of the clapper on the inside of the button bell sounded as loud as the bell in the distant church tower which we occasionally heard if the wind was blowing in our direction. Bells modulated the tenor of activity in the house; if the bells failed to evoke a response, she would tap and then rat-tat-tat on the floor with her cane. From the distance of the kitchen, the frequency of the rings or taps indicated, as with Morse code, a casual note or a more urgent telegram to the nether regions of the house.

I was frequently told that Grandmother, long a widow, had been a great beauty when young, as though that fact was explanation and excuse for any shortcomings she might have as an elderly woman. She had been noted for the luxuriance and rich copper of her hair, and this is what had attracted the eye of my grandfather when, as a dapper young *boulevardier*, he had returned from study in France to take up a teaching post in the Cork School of Art. Photographs show him as a young Parisian *flâneur*, a sleek Proustian young man in a jaunty fedora. Grandmother's hair had lost its wonderful hue but not its abundant growth. While she slept, I often crept close to the side of her bed and stared at the extraordinary coils which lay on her pillow in tumbling piles, like the sepia photographs of underwater sea-life I had seen in the copy of Arthur Mee's *Children's Encyclopaedia* which had belonged to my uncle when he was a boy. Sometimes, when the sound of her sleeping assured me that she would not awake, I liked to run my fingers along the coils of her hair. You could put your finger into the bottom of the coils as in a tube. One of her few activities when awake was to study her hair in an ornate silver hand-mirror, and to have it put up in what must have been the height of fashion when she was a young woman, with great tiers constructed like an inverted ziggurat. Her face, too, had not lost its beauty, and, despite the deep wrinkles of her skin and its almost translucent pallor, in repose she looked just like an elder version of the Sleeping Beauty in one of my storybooks. Although I knew, anecdotally, that she was my mother's mother, this seemed to me to be barely credible since she belonged to a time before time began, so ancient was she, as she lay immobile in marmoreal repose. I would have doubted that there could be anybody else in the world as old as Grandmother.

One feature of the room that I found endlessly sustaining was the radio. Unless my grandmother was awake, it couldn't be played loudly, but it could be turned on. The radio, like the rest of the furnishings, belonged to a bygone age, and was already an antique. When you turned a knob, initially nothing happened, but then, in the tiny fan-shaped window above the polished wooden knobs, a dim green light gradually became apparent until it reached its maximum brightness. More fascinating by far than waiting for the front dial to light up was to creep behind the marble-topped bureau on which the radio stood, and by looking into its inside, to watch the valves (bulbs which had a little twisted point of glass on the top) light up and begin to hum. Then the radio was ready to speak or to play music. I was not really interested in anything that the radio actually said, so much as the idea of its being able to have an independent existence in its polished mahogany cabinet. Above the dial was a panel of cloth behind criss-crossed timber bars, and if you held your hand to the cloth, it vibrated as the radio was speaking, got hot and, best of all, however low the sound, broke the silent monotony and darkness of the bedroom. When the radio was turned off, the light died away with infinite slowness and the heat and vibrations gradually ceased. The radio was my favourite object in the bedroom, and being able to turn it on had the added attraction of being an illicit activity since I was forbidden to play with the much grander radio at home.

Outside on the street, Mr McWilliams was making his way slowly up the opposite pavement. He shook constantly and his walking was erratic. He made little darts, this way and that, never proceeding in a straight line like other people. He also carried a walking stick but did not seem to use it and it hung from his damaged arm, waving about in unison with its owner's jerking pace. I had been told that Mr McWilliams had been in the trenches during the Great War and suffered from shell-shock: unaware that the Great War had ended a generation earlier, I assumed that this war was just another recent event. Most days he went up the far side of the street and, in the afternoon, returned with a companion on our side of the street. Mr McWilliams was one of a number of men in the neighbourhood with a similar condition: they all shook, lurched, or behaved strangely. I understood that they were neither mad nor dangerous, just incurably ill. Nonetheless, I regarded them with fear and suspicion, and if encountered out of doors, dodged behind whichever adult I was with in order not to come too close.

There were three zones in Grandmother's house: her bedroom, the rest of the house where one could poke about unsupervised, and the kitchen, the housekeeper's domain. If Grandmother was sleeping soundly, I could leave the room and try the doors on her landing, and the one below, and enter the rooms, each a little tomb of past life, full of old and interesting things, shelves laden with books and papers, art magazines, folios of prints and drawings, ceramics, woodcarvings, bric-à-brac, sagging furniture, all shrouded in dust and seen in the dim light of the partially obscured windows. On the half-landing hung life-size heads of women formed like corbels, jutting out from the walls. Originally I had assumed that, for reasons unexplained, their bodies were embedded within the walls, but later realized that they were merely pictures which stuck out. One of these, 'Lady Jennings as a bacchante', represented Grandfather's patron, who had been, according to Grandmother, a very gracious lady. Her head was, to me, decidedly peculiar, and whereas conventional people had hair or hats on their heads, Lady Jennings had bunches of grapes in profusion around her noble brows, with vine leaves and tendrils wandering around her neck. One day, and with great excitement, I managed, using a stepladder left unattended by some workman, to scramble up and have an eye-to-eye encounter with Lady Jennings, only to discover that she looked more like a girl's doll at close quarters than the lofty goddess she appeared to be from the half-landing.

On this floor was the bathroom, the most mysteriously shaped room in the house—L-shaped and as narrow and long as a corridor in some other building. Its passage led from the door to a right-angled turn, with another extended passage to what was known in Rosenheim as the lavatory, but in Windermere as the toilet, although it was the identical object. Well above my head height in these corridors, and intriguingly out of reach, were more bookshelves, but I was never able to discover what was on them. Adjoining the L-shaped room was Annie's room, which mostly contained Grandfather's papers. I never discovered the identity of this Annie who shared a name with the maid in Windermere, but since it was the only room to which a person's name was attached, I regarded her as a benign presence, and possibly still in residence.

To go farther down to the ground floor of the house meant encountering the only other occupants: Mrs Luby and Mary Brigid the maid. Mrs Luby presided in the kitchen, occasionally answered the front door, gave the maid orders, and prepared meals. She did not consider it appropriate that she should go upstairs, so all communications between Grandmother and the housekeeper were conveyed through the maid or by me. Mrs Luby, like a comic charwoman in a play, never removed her hat. When she arrived each day from her home in the nearby corporation redbrick terrace known as 'the buildings', the denizens of which lived in the perpetual lap of penury, she performed the same ritual of induction as she prepared for her day's tasks. Her coat was hung on the back of the scullery door, and from her bag she

removed and donned a striped apron; she then adjusted her hat before
the mirror, correctly positioning the fake pearl hatpins, and unfolded
Grandmother's newspaper, the *Cork Examiner*, which she placed on
the kitchen table. This was purchased daily in order that Grandmother
could keep abreast of the news, although she often dozed off by the time
the reader (sometimes my mother, usually the maid) had dealt with the
Deaths column and the main headlines. Now Mrs Luby was ready for
the day, and made the first of innumerable pots of strong tea. In repose,
her lined and care-worn face which I studied attentively when she was
absorbed in conversation and not looking in my direction, was of a
puce tint which reminded me of damson jam (there was a fine damson
tree in the back garden of Rosenheim), while the texture of her fingers
when she touched your skin had the abrasive feel of the sheets of rough
sandpaper in the garage at Windermere.

Mary Brigid, who lived-in, and occupied the maid's room upstairs,
next door to Grandmother's, came in for her day's orders and to chat
to Mrs Luby. I loved Mary Brigid because she was young, cheerful,
smiled a lot, and dressed in colourful clothes. She did not treat me as
Mrs Luby and all adults did—with suspicion that I had misbehaved,
or was about to do so. I often sat under the table and listened to the
two of them discussing the events of the neighbourhood, what Mrs
Luby had read in the newspaper, or local gossip. Mary Brigid too came
from the buildings, the principal staff resource for all the adjacent
residential streets, and the doings of the tenants was a perennial topic
for analysis: which husband had come home drunk again, which
woman was in the family way, who had lost his job in the brewery,
who was in jail for larceny or for grievous bodily harm. This narrative
of the wider world was a source of fascination to me, and the quieter
I sat, the less likely were the two women to censor their conversation.
It was Mrs Luby who enlightened me on the grotesque refinements of
trench warfare, expanding with grim relish on such topics as foot rot,
trench mouth, mustard or chlorine gas attacks, and infestations of

lice and vermin. For my grandmother, the Great War was a Homeric age of epic heroism and tragedy; for Mrs Luby, the topic presented an opportunity to dwell vicariously on the brute obscenities of war.

My maternal grandfather, in his first major sculptural commission, was carving the wall decoration in the sanctuary of Queenstown Cathedral, which had been rising over that seaport town since the eighteen sixties, when he spotted a young woman with gorgeous copper-coloured hair, wound in the Edwardian fashion, high on her head and as large as a hat. He followed her home, walking at a distance, and found that she lived in the oddest street in the town, West View, known for its curious appearance as 'the stack of cards'. This street is a terrace of identical Gothic-gabled houses, descending with a profile as jagged as an alligator's jaw, and while obviously a delightful example of architectural whimsy, can never have been an ideal place in which to live. In an obsessively hilly town where the streets wind languidly back and forth, effortlessly sidling up the slope, with all the houses facing out over the magnificent expanse of the harbour, West View, with a hard-to-explain perversity, heads directly up the hill to the summit at a suicidal incline, as though the houses imagined they were ascending the north face of the Eiger, making no concessions to human frailty or to the sheer instability of the street's appearance. In this fanciful abode, halfway up (or down) the precipitous slope, lived the girl with the wonderful hair.

Grandfather had just been appointed to his first teaching job in the Cork School of Art: Grandmother was an elocution and Montessori teacher. Both were handsome. To match her Catherine-wheel of hair, he sported a gallant handlebar moustache, the waxed points of which rivalled Lord Kitchener's. However, she refused to marry him, although he courted her determinedly. The memory of her dead first love deterred her from accepting any man's proposal and she kept him at bay for over five years, saying that she intended never to marry. When he threw himself in the harbour, she relented.

CHAPTER 2

As a small child, I experienced a dual existence, living both within and outside a dark painting that hung over the mantelpiece in my parents' drawing room. To my child's eye, the elements of the painting replicated those of my life in our home, and I could in my imagination move into the painting or emerge from it, bilocating with consummate ease, while sitting on the floor, playing with my toys or observing and listening to the adults talking. The work was a large reproduction known as a Medici print, framed in polished ebony-black lacquer, its subject a Dutch old master landscape of the seventeenth century by the artist Meindert Hobbema.

In *The Avenue, Middleharnis*, the view is a simple one of a long straight avenue disappearing away from the viewer, its verges lined by tall trees with bushy foliage at the tops, their trunks mostly bare. The colours of the painting are dark and sombre, not calculated to appeal to a small child, yet they were evidently no deterrent to my interest. Water-filled dykes border the avenue in the painting and to either side of the flat landscape are the tree-farms where miniature versions of the mature trees of the avenue are being grown. On the right, a man in a floppy hat is tending the saplings. In the distance is a town or village, the tower of its church rising golden over the browns, dark greens and greys of the landscape. In a perfect and unconscious exercise in anthropomorphism, I inserted my domestic world into the picture, and its principal elements became visual symbols of the tangible world of my family which surrounded me.

The two tallest trees in the foreground, one with a round cropped head of foliage, the other with more flowing leaves, I understood to be my parents—the cropped tree my father's tight military hairstyle, the more lush, my mother's Vera Lynn wartime tresses of auburn hair. A formation of trees at the end of the avenue became a leaping image of our Kerry Blue terrier, Blitz, a dog who barked in tune with the music of the time. The treetops directly behind my father, which had a more florid profile, were my aunt, my mother's elder sister, always referred to as 'the aunt'. My older brother and I were represented by the presence of the miniature trees, standing in the protective care of the adult ones, the balance and continuity of nature in the painting reflecting that of the real world. As I sat on the floor of the drawing room, looking up at the painting, it projected an image of security and immutability, as tangible to me as anything experienced in daily life.

Having many years later seen the original painting in the National Gallery in London and looking today at photographs of my parents taken during that time—the middle years of World War II, the appositeness of my identifying them as the parent trees of the painting is striking. I never confided this child's-eye view of my familiar world to anyone because it required neither verification nor comment. That what I saw was invisible to others would not have struck me: presence and transference into the painting being a simultaneous experience, beyond the need of justification or proof. Hobbema's *The Avenue, Middleharnis* followed my family's progress through numerous houses and continued to be for me a refuge of calm, even when I no longer dwelled within its certainties.

Later, in the same effortless manner in which I passed between the physical world of the family drawing room and the metaphysical one of occupying a place in the painting, I passed between Rosenheim, my grandmother's house, and my parents' Windermere without seriously challenging the radical divergence of these realms. Between the two houses were four streets, counting Grandmother's and ours, neatly arranged in a perfect zigzag pattern. In Windermere, we lived at the dog-leg, as I often heard my parents describe it. Our street was bordered by a high wall on one side and market gardens on the other, until Windermere was reached at the corner. I consulted with Blitz on the issue of the dog-leg but he provided no enlightenment. I scrutinized every dog I passed or that peered in our gate from the pavement or peed on its pillars, but never encountered one that had legs the shape of our street. The house's original owners had named it 'Windermere' and so it remained throughout our life there. The body of water in England's Lake District, after which it was called, was to my mother a pleasing Wordsworthian allusion. However, at the bottom of the street lay a small artificial lake with an island of duck-concealing reeds at its centre, far removed from the broad expanses of Lake Windermere, but which, in a moment of proprietorial irony, may have provided a more mundane prompt for the naming of the house.

From the dog-leg and its houseless expanse, the next street had houses behind high walls, some terraces and a shop into which we never went, although it would have been convenient because we passed it so frequently. Women, usually the owners, served behind the counter of all the local small shops. In this case and most others, my mother said, 'We shall not shop there; the woman is inquisitive'. By this evaluation, almost every local grocery shop failed her strict criteria, the nosy parker being the nadir in her concept of undesirable people. The maids in my grandmother's house and in ours had instructions never to enter numerous of the local shops on account of their owners being gossips, precisely the factor that made them attractive as a source of news and neighbourhood scandal. Around the corner from the principal forbidden shop was another street, this one quite narrow and of no interest. It led to Grandmother's street and Rosenheim, called after the town of Rosenheim in Bavaria, a watering place with famous sulphur baths (and coincidentally the birthplace of Hermann Goering). Between Windermere and Rosenheim, England and Germany, my world was contained by these contrastingly elusive and foreign-sounding points of reference: it was only during the final years of World War II that it dawned upon me that we lived in Ireland and not in one of these two warring nations. The only explanation I could offer to appease my parents' incredulity at this lapse was that they had managed to omit mention of this salient point of local geography.

How reliable is memory? An unanswerable question when there is a lapse of a lifetime between the remembrance and the events remembered: the memories may be accurate or imagined, or be of events recounted by family members rather than personally experienced, most probably a melange of all three, impossible to unpick. There are other sources of remembrance—those who were there too—but their memories will most probably differ from one's own to the point of near total contradiction. There is also photography. My father had been a serious photographer since his youth, and his images neatly divide the early stages of his life into leisure and art. Beach scenes with friends, crowds of happy cloche-hatted women, and men with unkempt hair sitting on strands in windswept locations are typical of his casual photography. These are in marked contrast to the art photographs of carefully composed still lifes, single figures in brooding lighting conditions, stark images of himself or other young men, laden with melancholy or angst-ridden expressions.

When he was pursuing my mother, he became a devotee of her image, and she appears in countless shots, the type of classic Irish face beloved of artists seeking images of Celtic spirituality. She was moodily distant and intangible, a manner she strove to maintain throughout her life. She never smiled in photographs and so presents the aura of some ethereal Pre-Raphaelite muse, probably due for an early grave (which was not to be the case). My mother attributed her unquestioned vagueness and the distance she maintained between herself and others to the banality of having suffered concussion while a student when she fell off a bus. Whether this was true, or a subterfuge to disguise a natural aloofness, never became clear. My father transferred his observations to his sons, and my brother and I became the principal subject of his domestic photographs, while his military life became the focus for the rest of his camera work: the youthful crowds and self-regarding solitary males were seen no more.

My brother and I were photographed as though a symbiotic couple, non-identical twins, forever together, forever identically dressed in shapeless hand-knitted pullovers, forever engaged in the same activities, myself the dark-haired, brown-eyed, shorter one, my brother the taller, blond-haired and grey-eyed. The photographs became variations on a theme, repeated with daunting determination, from when we were infants to the time, some ten years later, when my father suddenly stopped taking photographs. These images of childhood now form a useful adjunct to memory and confirm the basic facts of existence, that I was then as I now remember, and my brother likewise. Some credence therefore must be placed in the veracity of personal memory, and even when unsupported by corroborative evidence, it is the greatest individual resource we possess. Yet in most of my memories, my supposedly inseparable sibling is not there in the angle of my vision, although he doubtless was present on most occasions. The camera, which in the mid-twentieth century was less inclined to lie than in the early twenty-first, testifies to his being always at my side. Perhaps, as children close in age, we were in my thinking as one person, although the divergence of our characters suggests otherwise.

CHAPTER 3

At a gesture from Mrs Luby in response to the ringing doorbell, Mary Brigid went up the long dim hallway to the front door. Despite some light filtering through the panels of coloured glass in the front door, the hall was the darkest space in the house. A heavy gloom, sustained by brown embossed wallpaper above the dado rail and timber panelling below it, was compounded by the dividing velvet curtains. These hung between the outer and inner hall, and exuded a rank smell of must, smoke and age. The curtains were of a deep maroon, shading towards indigo, with rows of bobbles suspended from the selvedge. Occasionally I would detach one of these little furry balls and carry it off to Windermere as a keepsake, until caught in the act by Mrs Luby. The curtains hung three-quarters of the way across the passage, excluding nearly all the light from the inner doors, and their bobbles would caress your cheek as you passed, like soft fingertips. The curtains had to be negotiated in order to get to the front door; the next obstacle was the hallstand which carried an array of hats, overcoats, canes, galoshes and umbrellas capable of equipping a substantial household.

If the caller was one of Mrs Luby's female visitors, she was brought down by Mary Brigid and joined us in the kitchen for more tea; Mrs Dalton, Mrs Therbarry, Mrs Slyne were Mrs Luby's most frequent visitors, all residents of and professional colleagues from the buildings. The housekeeper used the kitchen for entertaining and impressing her peers, women who cleaned or 'did' in the bigger houses of the neighbourhood: she considered, in the protocols of menial work, that housekeeping and 'doing' were high status positions, vastly superior to the mere maids, who were young, hardly literate, and of questionable character. Her cronies sat, coats off, hats on, and reprised the doings of the locality, drank copious cups of tea, ate brown bread and butter, and relished the heat from the range. The temperature of the kitchen was by many degrees hotter than in any other part of the house, unheated except for the fire in the old woman's bedroom. This was tended by Mary Brigid, whose duties included lugging buckets of coal upstairs. As well as all other household tasks and the shopping, she was responsible for rising early in the morning in order to light the range. Mrs Luby merely presided. When anything was required for the house or for Mrs Luby's private use, the maid was sent on errands, on which I occasionally was allowed to accompany her.

Mary Brigid was more an observer than a participant in Mrs Luby's social circle. She listened and occasionally contributed, but was probably lacking in that first essential of the gossip: curiosity. Where I would have liked to ask questions, only to be told that it did not concern me, or just to be quiet, Mary Brigid, who could legitimately have asked all sorts of interesting questions, remained silent, ruminating over her cup of tea and resting her feet. Her horizon was confined to the low redbrick contours of the buildings and nothing that happened any farther afield engaged her. Yet she was kind to me in a casual manner, praising me when Mrs Luby habitually found fault, slipping me extra biscuits under the table, encouraging the housekeeper to allow me out on errands with her.

Mrs Luby's talents hardly extended beyond keeping a weather eye on the changing list of housemaids, periodically dismissed for minor misdemeanours, petty dishonesty or being incompetent to perform the most basic household tasks. Often they just fled from her viscous tongue and clacking criticism. During the housekeeper's reign, there had been numerous young girls employed, each dismissed after a period when Mrs Luby wished to promote a new candidate and demonstrate her influence to less favoured neighbours. It was a given in Mrs Luby's world view that all young women were morally lax: she encouraged the maids to expand on their love life, then dismissed them for what had been revealed.

However, Mrs Luby baked excellent wholemeal brown bread, her most valued contribution to the functioning of the household. Following tea, instructions to the maid, the jotting down of a shopping list, orders to me to stay in Grandmother's room and not to be prying or making noise, she donned her extra calico apron and prepared the day's bread while the oven heated up. The number of loaves baked was quite disproportionate to the needs of Mary Brigid, Mrs Luby, myself and to Grandmother, who ate hardly anything. There was the loaf for Mrs Luby to take home, the loaf for her sister's large family, and sometimes one for Mary Brigid's family in the buildings, delivered by the housekeeper as an act of beneficent patronage. Mrs Luby regarded herself as 'a great provider', even if my grandmother's purse was the source of all the provisions and the beneficiaries not members of her employer's family. As if by clockwork, not long after the bread had emerged from the oven, the doorbell would ring, and Mary Brigid would usher in one or more of Mrs Luby's colleagues. Tea and hot buttered bread were dispensed to the visitors.

Whenever my mother's older brother came to visit us in Windermere, generally about once or twice a year because he lived in a more distant county, he invariably remarked, following a visit to Rosenheim, 'Mrs Luby will have to go. That woman has no regard for the truth and is a bad influence on those around her.' My parents also heartily disliked Mrs

Luby, and required little prompting: shortly afterwards the housekeeper would receive her notice. Often, by misfortune or by calculation, this would coincide with the departure or firing of the maid of the day, making it imperative for the housekeeper to remain, at least temporarily. This charade occurred with some regularity: the uncle would denounce Mrs Luby and notice would be given, only to be rescinded for pragmatic reasons. Then she might be fired again for some new failing, other than her habitual dishonesty, and actually leave. But she always returned, generally following the failure of her replacement to even measure up to Mrs Luby's highly porous standards. After each dismissal, the housekeeper retired to the buildings and awaited a summons to return. Pride being an important asset in these circumstances, a refusal to return had to be met by some inducement, such as an offer of increased wages. She regarded herself as indispensable and her reinstatement inevitable. Experience tended to confirm her analysis.

There was a tinkling of bells and I scampered up the stairs and quietly let myself into Grandmother's room. She was awake, cross-looking and had the Dutch Boy by the head, wielding him with unexpected energy. She stared at me accusingly and began her customary interrogation.

'What were you doing, boy? Listening to Mrs Luby's stupid tittle-tattle I suppose. Evil-minded old harridan. Where is Mary Brigid? Go and fetch her. I want my hair combed now. Boy, what are you waiting for? Go!'

I ran down, two steps at a time, to Mary Brigid, who, with a poor grace, brushed the crumbs from her lips and followed me back upstairs. The ritual of hair-combing was always a pleasure to watch, as Grandmother sat upright against a mass of pillows and Mary Brigid began her work. First, the great inverted pyramid of hair had to be let down, then its individual coils separated and slowly combed. The whole operation took about an hour, during which Grandmother would doze off while remaining bolt upright. When the coils, which seemed too numerous to count, had been combed, they were rolled on a pair of curling tongs, heated over a small cut-glass spirit stove that sat amongst the bells. The tiny blue flame of the methylated spirits faded and grew with every movement of air. By the time the coils had been returned to their correct mounting, the old woman was tired and dismissed Mary Brigid peremptorily.

'Go now, and you, boy, don't be troublesome or I will have to speak to your mother.'

Being troublesome might include tiptoeing into the front room on the ground floor where the tick of the cuckoo-clock rhythmically sounded in the stillness. Taking one of Grandmother's walking canes from the hallstand, I could, by reaching up on tiptoe, advance the hands of the clock so that a small door would spring open and the delightful little cuckoo, with its bright red open beak, suddenly would emerge from its nest, declaiming loudly. I found this sensation so riveting that I might gently move the hands on a further hour and look and listen again to the small bird's call. I refused to believe that it was operated mechanically and was not in fact a real bird. The speed of its appearance and departure and the startling sweetness of its voice were such that one had to believe it was real. While engaged in enticing the cuckoo out of its nest, I had to be careful that Grandmother, supposedly sleeping upstairs, was indeed soundly asleep; otherwise, she would hear the sharp 'cuck-oo' in the distance and be furious that I had disobeyed her. Then the bells would ring and the cane begin to send Morse code on the floor and Mrs Luby or Mary Brigid would come to reprimand me for disturbing their employer, and more particularly, themselves.

When I resumed my seat at the window and surveyed the street, the 'shell-shocked' Mr McWilliams was returning from his outing, this time on the Rosenheim side of the street. I had been to many beaches and had a collection of shells, both found locally and exotically, but there appeared nothing threatening about them. It was just one of those many aspects of the adult world which mostly nobody chose to explain, until Mrs Luby had done me the honour. Mr McWilliams often came back with a companion, not shell-shocked and quivering, but in need of two limbs, an arm and a leg. This was Mr Daly. Considering his disadvantages, he was far steadier on his one foot than Mr McWilliams on two, and bounded along with a crutch to replace his missing limb, with flapping folded-over sleeve and trouser-leg to indicate the missing parts. By good fortune (if such a grim misadventure can be so described), he had lost limbs on opposite sides. I had been told that he also had been in the trenches of the Great War, with the Munsters at Gallipoli. The two trenchmen always crossed the street diagonally opposite Rosenheim, Mr McWilliams with zig-zagging gait, Mr Daly in energetic strides, and went in Mr McWilliams' front door which was opened by Bessie the maid, a friend of Mary Brigid's. On their afternoon off, the maids went to the cinema together. I looked forward to these outings because on the following day, Mary Brigid would enthusiastically recount the entire story of the film they had seen, with appropriate dramatic effects, exhaustive detail and dialogue. Although I had never been to the cinema, I became a connoisseur of the stars of the silver screen, of their interesting and complicated private lives, and of the theme songs, sung by Mary Brigid for my benefit.

I had listened to Grandmother's monologues for a long time before they began to make any sense. Her narrations, like much adult conversation, seemed perpetually to be concentrated on some topic of which others were informed and of which I knew nothing. Only by continual alertness and the repetition of the topics and questioning of my mother or the kitchen staff in Rosenheim did I gradually begin to unravel the riddles of Grandmother's talk and phraseology. She could in a single sentence combine 'the dear boys' and 'the dear knows' and 'dear me' without any indication to me as to the distinction between the lost beloved, the good Lord and an expression of mild unease. Only much later did I understand that 'the dear boys' were those who had fallen at the Somme, Ypres and the Dardanelles, whose passing became a life-long touchstone for her grief.

Grandmother grew up in the seaport of Queenstown, some fifteen miles south-east of Cork city. On the establishment of the Irish Free State in 1922, the local Urban District Council had changed the name of the town to Cóbh (pronounced 'cove' but with the Gaelicized spelling of the English word). Grandmother resolutely refused to adopt what she regarded as the absurdity of the altered name, remaining a citizen of Queenstown until her death. As a former teacher, her interest in language prompted her to demote the hated Cóbh to the risible phonetic Kob-h. Her sarcastic pronunciation for her renamed hometown was used when wishing to refer to some further decline in taste or fall from grace on behalf of its civic authorities or population, for which there were frequent opportunities. In the mouths of its citizens the town continues its existence as plain Cove, spelled Cobh but without the accent, the UDC's initiative successful in that the use of Queenstown died with Grandmother's generation.

Queenstown had its royal name bestowed on it by Queen Victoria following her visit to the town in 1849 at the end of the Great Famine, from which she, perhaps unknown to herself, acquired the title of 'the Famine Queen'. The harbour was then, and continued to be into the early years of the twentieth century, a great marshalling port for the British Navy. Flotillas lay at anchor there throughout my grandmother's childhood, forming a backdrop to the town's significance as one of the maritime sights of the Victorian age. She grew up with the sea at her doorstep and mythologized the life of the fisherman and the navy, presenting them to me as some idyllic vision of a life more worth living. She knew the names of ships long lost to the waves, torpedoed or wrecked in storms, with great loss of life, and had arcane information on the movements of troopships to South Africa and ports from Sebastopol to Colombo. At times she would intone the names of the *Ajax*, the *Ibis*, the *Nimrod* and the *Sirius* as though they had been the guardians at her cradle.

One of her brothers had been drowned in a boating accident when a boy and her attitude to the sea was a contradictory one of fascination and fear. She talked to me as though I was destined for a life at sea and was full of imprecations on the dangers of the deep, as well as its charms.

'When you are in a rowboat, boy, lie back and let your hands glide in the cold of the water. It's a delightful sensation', doubtless remembering when she had been a demure Edwardian miss in a long white muslin dress and broad-brimmed hat, being rowed in the bay, her hand languidly tracing a pattern on the surface of the water, with in the distance the Dreadnoughts and ships of the line, crewed by sailors in starched white uniforms, doing hornpipes on the deck as though in the chorus of a Savoy operetta.

Grandmother's influence on my family's life in Windermere was one of representing standards never to be attained, and my mother's efforts to satisfy her own mother's criteria were doomed to failure. In circumstances of which I have no knowledge, my grandmother chose both my brother's and my own first names, although these have no precedent in the names of either of my parents' families, where names were ritualistically repeated for generations. For this, no explanation is forthcoming beyond Grandmother's supreme sense of her own moral authority and her ability to have this accepted as a norm of behaviour. Having spent her childhood in Queenstown as a bastion of Empire, she carried very clear ideas of propriety and decorum, and while she would never have invoked the old queen's days as an example of an idyllic age, she nonetheless never quite left behind Victorian sentiment and rigour, believing that a straight back and a clear gaze represented a good front to the world.

CHAPTER 4

By the time I had become an almost daily fixture at Rosenheim, Grandmother no longer left the house. A year or so earlier, when she was less housebound, she occasionally decided to visit Windermere if weather and other oracles coincided to recommend a favourable passage. Mrs Luby and my mother were united in very little, but concurred in the belief that Grandmother should not be encouraged to go visiting. Every time she announced her intention to go visiting, Mrs Luby mentioned the imminent prospect of heavy rain, the old woman's sciatica and lumbago, despite the evidence that the sun was scorching the paving slabs in the street and melting the tarmac. To Mrs Luby, the elderly should know their place and, when ill, remain indoors: to my mother, the prospect of her own mother collapsing on the road and the ensuing drama involving opportunistic nosy-parkers and do-gooders was enough to send her to bed with a migraine.

When Grandmother was determined to emerge, the procedure was a tortuous ritual of preparation and gathering all that had to be brought to accompany the journey. It was unthinkable that she should go alone: she travelled with as large an entourage as could be assembled; all were bidden to support her progress. If her ideas of decorum and order devolved from the late nineteenth century when the old queen had reigned for more than sixty glorious years, her dress sense belonged to the same era. Black was her signature colour, either as the widow of her late husband, or because she was still in nominal mourning for the death of Victoria's consort Prince Albert, an event that occurred before she was born. Her ankle-length dresses were striped or polka-dotted in shades of gray, black or a deep Prussian blue, quite jazzy designs rendered sombre by the pervasive colour range. Over the dress with trailing fringes she donned her enormous Siberian overcoat, which reached almost to the ground, its fur trim brushing her shoes. Around the neck of this coat was a pack of six fox-furs, their alert little heads, with sharply glinting glass eyes, bobbing as she walked, their brushes hanging down around her arms. I greatly admired these foxes and was convinced that when a stray dog was encountered on the road, the foxes' ears would prick up in anticipation of trouble. On her head she wore a black pot hat, remote ancestor of the cloche, enmeshed in netting and secured with lengthy pins of jet, so black and shiny that they flashed in the sunlight. She stood erect and bone thin in this apparel, and was ready to set out, her pair of brass-ferruled walking canes tap-tapping along the pavement. The sheer weight of the coven of vixen, in addition to the enormous coat she was wearing, would have daunted most people intending to go for a stroll in a midsummer heatwave, but she appeared oblivious of the high temperature which was sapping the energy of passers-by, driving the more hedonistic to sleep off the afternoon in back gardens or on coastal beaches, gasping in the heat.

Grandmother led, Mrs Luby followed, carrying her medicines, and the maid of the day strolled behind carrying a muffler and rugs in case a breeze should somehow manage to move in the dead air of an August afternoon. Then came the element that my mother dreaded most when she herself was a member of the entourage: Grandmother was an Olympic standard slow walker. She proceeded at such a remarkably restrained pace that she appeared not to be moving at all, and the fur-lined hem of her coat merely floated over the road surface like the frills of a hovercraft, its motive power invisible and at exceptionally low revs. For the less halt to move at a similar pace was impossible, so the bond servants circled around her, falling over themselves and each other in a state of protracted ennui. The five-minute walk to Windermere could take an hour, and if, as usually happened, some neighbour or distant acquaintance was encountered, the tragedies of the century had to be rehearsed, and the more recently dead accounted for, the dying lamented. Then we might proceed another few yards before she decided to stop again for a rest.

Inevitably, some of her most favoured walking wounded were met, and no matter how impossible it was for Mr Daventry or old Mr Pulvertaft to utter two consecutive shell-shocked syllables, Grandmother was determined to engage them in exacting conversation concerning their families, their own physical condition and remembrance of things passed. These encounters made the difficult journey even more intolerable for her escort, forced to watch the now elderly dear boys from the trenches squirm with embarrassment as they failed to assemble a single conversational sentence. Goodbyes were said and we continued. Mr McWillams, one of the loquacious wounded, long considered to be a close family friend, although he never in my experience visited Rosenheim, was a treasured encounter on these occasional walks. Grandmother found conversation with him most satisfactory, and much information was exchanged on the same topics of the dead, the damaged and the dying.

By the time we got to Windermere, I had been climbing garden walls and scaling railings in an effort to relieve the boredom, the maid left behind, as statuesque as Lot's wife, daydreaming in the middle of the sun-baked street, and Mrs Luby po-faced as she woefully regretted the loss of an afternoon's gossip and the unnecessary expenditure of energy.

My mother, knowing the prearranged time of Grandmother's departure from Rosenheim, and calculating the rate of progress, would come forward to join us, having decided that her mother had probably collapsed in the heat and was lying comatose on the pavement, being gaped at by strangers. Eventually our destination was sighted and the resilient old woman, tired from her walk but having developed a healthy appetite, picked up a head of steam at the prospect of her tea. The meal had to be served with appropriate decorum: the silver tea service, the fine bone china, paper doilies on the bread and cake plates, milk in first of course, us children banished. In such circumstances, her conversation would become even more meandering and nostalgic, stimulated by having emerged from her habitual environment of drawn curtains, dark rooms and soporific inertia.

The effort required for the passage between the two houses had exhausted Grandmother and if she moved slowly on the outward journey, she returned by almost standing still, her feet moving invisibly in ever-smaller steps, until she was in fact stationary for much of the time. Back in her own house, the strain of the outing sent her immediately to bed, with warnings to me to be quiet, to sit still, not to be running about the house. With most of her contemporaries dead or no longer in circulation, these trips were the last excursions of her life, carried out in defiance of her daughter's protests, barely postponing her looming incarceration, which followed within weeks of her last journeys.

CHAPTER 5

My mother considered children to be female by definition: little girls were of the sweet and doll-playing variety, devoted to domestic sentiments and possessed of placid natures. When, some years after her marriage, she found herself in possession of two male children, she was dismayed. Although she had an elder brother who, following their father's death, occupied the role of substitute father figure during her teenage years, she had little understanding of the male psyche and, as a species, did not empathize with small boys very much. In fact she regarded their behaviour as alarming and inexplicable. As my brother and I grew older, she found herself confronted by two inscrutable and alien beings whose mentality baffled her, one a confrontational child who asked awkward questions in a high and penetrating voice, the other (myself) who smiled benignly but took no notice of her and kept his own counsel. The fact that her house was occupied by these foreign souls was tantamount to an invasion of the privacy of her life, and the thwarting of her maternal ambitions to nurture a brood of young princesses, adept in house management, baking and social skills. It was not what she had foreseen and, fate having played a nasty trick upon her, she was at a loss as to how the matter might be dealt with. Consulting her husband about her difficulties proved unhelpful.

Being a good needlewoman and enjoying dressmaking for herself, she made clothes for her children when they were young. She also made dolls. Not having girls, she could hardly make conventional girl-dolls so she devised a compromise approach, creating *Wind in the Willows*-like animals, upright and colourfully dressed, as playthings for her sons. These soft toys accompanied me for all my childhood without my ever realizing that at the time they represented uncommon playthings for boy-children. My favourite, which lasted until I was ten or eleven, was named Louis Lapin, a tall and improbable rabbit, closer to the creations of Maurice Sendak than Kenneth Grahame. Louis had a bright plaid waistcoat with pearl buttons, gray felt trousers and a flat cap with a pom-pom. His floppy ears were almost as long as his arms. These toys were never allowed out of the house, suggesting that my mother may have been aware that society (the neighbours) might consider them a reason for adverse comment.

Coming from a late Victorian social structure in her own home where the paterfamilias was loved, admired and respected, she conferred on my father the same status of patriarch. Since he himself shared these values, even if his standpoint was more a response to military discipline than nineteenth-century social mores, they were at one in their definition of the male presence in the household. Unfortunately, boys had not in my mother's experience been part of the familial structure and she commenced a protracted struggle to understand the demons to which she had given birth. Her love for her family was without bounds, but she might have been more contented had the gender war not begun so early in her career of motherhood. Since my mother was without guile, she was a perfect target for being tested; in battles of the will she fared badly, often losing to her child-adversaries.

When my brother and I were quite small, male destructive capability had already declared itself. The aunt, always a beneficent guest, had just departed, leaving an expensive collection of children's toys suitable for young boys, model cars with which one might go varooming around on the carpet. Having seen her sister leave, my mother became aware of loud smashing sounds coming from the upstairs landing where my brother and I were happily engaged with hammers, smashing the toy cars in a mood of hilarious glee. As my mother grabbed the hammers and gazed dumbfoundedly at her sister's gift, the damaged evidence of which would now have to be concealed, she asked what was going on. Proudly we chorused, 'Oh, we're wreckers.'

Milk was delivered by horse and cart from a dairy in a nearby street. Whether the dairy-man's cows grazed unseen behind the house, or in fields elsewhere, I never discovered. We passed near the dairy whenever we made the journey from Windermere to Rosenheim. All I knew was that, promptly at the same hour every day, the milkman would arrive outside our gate with his horse-drawn trap, adapted to hold two large metal churns, with the delivery taps protruding through holes cut in the rear panelling of the cabin. Women, girls, maids would emerge from the houses with ceramic jugs and galvanized gallon cans to collect the milk, which was dispensed in an attractive hissing stream of milky foam into the containers. From the security of our gate, I watched this operation with intense interest, and would have liked to be in charge of it myself. The horse trotted amiably from gate to gate, stopped in answer to commands from the milkman, and ambled on again as instructed. Annie stood still as her gallon jug was filled, then returned to the house with the heavy vessel of fresh creamy milk, bubbling on the surface.

The milkman's commands to his horse intrigued me. If the owner said 'Yup', the horse would move on; it would stop at the sound of 'Whoa'. It was very simple and elegant to my ear, and like Blitz, whom

I was convinced understood human speech perfectly, I had no doubt that the milkman's horse possessed an extensive equine vocabulary. I went around the garden chanting 'Yup, Whoa' to myself until I felt that I had got the sounds to perfection. Having thoroughly learned my horse-language, I then had to put it to use and tried the words on Blitz, but without any evident success. The dog merely looked at me and yawned. Following chanting visits to the kitchen where the maid was busy, and to the dining room where my mother was writing letters, I was ejected from each in turn and told to go to the garden, play in my wigwam and not be such a nuisance.

Days of practising horse-talk had made me neigh-perfect. As usual, Annie stood on the pavement outside our front gate, a tall ceramic jug with blue and white horizontal bands held out to the milkman, who took it and filled it from one of his two taps. Following his milk delivery on Fridays, the milkman, wearing a sepia-coloured linen coat and flat cap, would go from door to door, settling his weekly accounts, leaving horse and cart standing unattended in the practically trafficless wartime street. The milkman was an affable individual and enjoyed chatting and joking with his customers. While he was talking, I slipped out the gate and put my two tasks into operation: to turn on the milk jet, and to speak to the horse. Unfortunately, I had neglected the significant part in the ritual played by the jug.

With milk streaming on to the street, I got such a fright that I yelled 'Yup, Yup' as loudly as I could, and ran for the gate. The horse, obedient to command, trotted off down the hill, milk streaming behind. Women awaiting the daily delivery farther down the street shrieked for the milkman, who emerged from a house, yelling 'Whoa, Whoa', at which the horse slowed his pace and came to a halt, halfway down the hill. Some passer-by turned off the milk jet, which had left a strong white river running from our gate and passing the cart. While some man had stepped from the gathering crowd to hold the horse's reins, the milkman came to our front door to remonstrate and demand restitution. My mother was appalled and in tears. She paid the milkman for a few gallons of wasted milk, cringed with embarrassment, and went in search of the culprit. Since nearly everyone else on the street had witnessed my crime, denial was impossible. She ran me to ground in my wigwam at the bottom of the back garden, and demanded to know why I had done such an outrageous thing, insisting that I should apologize to the milkman the following morning. All I could suggest was that I wanted to see what would happen.

Later, confined to quarters, as I glumly stared out of the bedroom window at the street, she returned downstairs, ruminating on the fact that a little girl would never have behaved so meanly. During the war years, waste was strongly disapproved of, and when I was summoned on the following morning for my formal apology to the milkman, he scowled at me. 'Behaviour worthy of a cornerboy' was his verdict. Twice over, my mother had been humiliated, her child's public misbehaviour followed by the milkman's verdict were as cutting an indictment of her motherhood as she could have received.

If my interest in horse-talk and the technology of brass taps was in the realm of dedicated scientific investigation, my brother's antipathy for the coal delivery man's boy was more personal. Like the milk, fuel was delivered by horse and cart, pulled not by a handsome pony, but in this case by an elderly and asthmatic dray horse, dragging a float stacked high with sacks of coal or turf, and with neatly arranged bundles of chopped wood. I didn't care for these proceedings because they were so dirty and so I took myself off upstairs to observe the sacks being carried in the side gate on the coalman's back, and emptied over his head into the coalhouse. The coalman's uniform of a coal sack worn on the head like a monk's cowl added a sinister aspect to the operation. The apprentice, christened 'Block' by my brother, brought in the lighter and smaller bundles of wood. Both coalman and Block looked as if they had been made up for a *Black and White Minstrel show*, their sooty, coal-begrimed faces enlivened by pink mouths and white staring eyes, their clothes as dirty as the coal sacks. My brother clearly found these denizens of the lower depths aesthetically unpleasing and concentrated his animosity on the unfortunate Block, whose permanently running nose, hands purple with cold, and filthy clothes (which were most probably the rags he wore to school) hardly made him more attractive. Whether the child was the son of the coalheaver or a sorcerer's apprentice was unknown.

Inclined to be more provocative than me, my brother just did not like the black-faced boy and may not have appreciated the appearance of another boy, however briefly, in what he perceived as his territory (I presented no challenge whatsoever to his ascendancy). As the boy came and went, my brother stood at a safe distance, pointed at him accusingly and yelled 'Ho, Block!', in itself meaningless, but it was received as intended and the exceptionally wiry and street-smart Block took serious umbrage. He went back and forth, carrying the bales of wood, while my brother stood in the yard yelling 'Ho, Block!' every time he passed. After half a dozen journeys, during which he had to endure the taunting, Block answered his persecutor very effectively by flinging a small log at him, followed by another and another which, probably intentionally, missed their target, but smashed panes in the glasshouse. The sound of breaking glass, Block's outraged shouting and my brother's terrified screams, brought my mother, Annie and the coalheaver running, as Block's armoury of hunks of wood shot past my brother's head, and sent shards flying.

My mother's attitude to the downtrodden was one of compassionate concern, compromised by a desire to separate herself from conflict and displays of impoverishment as quickly as possible. She appeased the coalman with a cup of tea served in the yard, apologized to Block and gave him a shilling, regretted the broken panes and sent for my brother to explain his behaviour, which he refused to do. To this impasse there was no immediate solution. Block and his master left, the boy to get a beating from the coalheaver. My brother was sent to his bedroom, while my mother contemplated what explanation she would give her husband for the damaged glasshouse. Again she considered the enigma of the man-child and sighed in desperation.

When my father came home, she lamented bitterly about the day's doings and the sheer impossibility of controlling the children. Occasionally my father would mount the stairs, four steps at a go, and roar at the culprit; mostly he just laughed and opened his newspaper. As a child himself of a large family of boys, and used to the violent and abusive behaviour of soldiers, he took a benign view of his sons' antics. However, when he later saw the smashed glass in the glasshouse, he found the matter less amusing.

The drama that surrounded the lives of the staff in Rosenheim was without evident parallel in Windermere. My parents were the focus of our lives and of the household, whereas in Rosenheim Mrs Luby and the maid's presence expanded to fill a vacuum in authority: this gave them freedom to live according to their own inclinations. In our house, the maid was very much in the background, an essential element in the fabric of the family, but divided from it by class and education. No great events or adventures surrounded the maid's life, or if they did I never got to hear of them. Unlike in Rosenheim, the Windermere maid opened no doors and no unknown realms of life were introduced to me by their conversation, mostly overheard or supervised by my mother. Furthermore, the Windermere regime maintained a servant's dress code that did not prevail in Rosenheim where more slatternly attire was accepted. In Windermere the maid, always aproned, changed her dress and apron from the morning's wear if my mother was expecting guests—even the aunt was regarded as a guest. Formal afternoon wear consisted of a knee-length black dress, white starched miniature apron, suitable (minus the dress) for floor shows in a Las Vegas casino, and an improbable hairpiece of starched spiky fabric which stuck up in the air like the paper band around a Christmas cake. Thus accoutred, Annie was fit to answer the door and serve tea to visiting ladies. Whether or not she, her predecessors and successors had any social life, or even anything to call a private life, is debatable. Permanently at their employer's call, they had no free time other than one afternoon off per week. More akin to being held on remand than in slavery, the domestic maid was such a commonplace that the iniquity of their lives was hardly visible. In the novels of the early to mid-twentieth century, domestic help is ubiquitous, part of the furniture of life. Even in the cartoons of Heath Robinson, it is frequently the maid who provides the motor power for the artist's fanciful contraptions. Being 'in service' gave employment to young women lacking in education or work skills, and was sufficiently widespread that it must have been mutually beneficial, even if exploitative.

Lizzie, Gracie, Elizabeth and Annie are a succession of our maid's names. Did they come in that order and for how long did they remain with us? I cannot tell. A distinction between our maids and Grandmother's is that hers were local girls from the buildings, used to city life and assertively independent, whereas ours were mostly country girls, brought specifically from the farm, recommended by someone with whom my mother had some distant connection. They lacked the network of contacts which the city girls had and were constrained by their duties and the sense of clockwork order (as well as the absence of opportunities for dissent) which prevailed in our household. To some farm girl, expected when at home to rise at dawn every day to help with the milking, the *modus operandi* at Windermere presented no great labour or difficulty and the maids fitted in to the ordained scheme of things, or else quickly departed. Politeness, respect and willingness were expected of them, and long hours.

My mother's attitude to these girls was ambiguous, half-patronizing them as ignorant young women in need of being 'brought on' in the sense of improving themselves and their domestic skills, fitting them for marriage, and embarrassed by having the intimacies of her personal life exposed to strangers. She didn't really like the idea of domestic staff, and, instead of being open and friendly, even at such close quarters, she kept her distance. In the Victorian upstairs-downstairs world of large, many-roomed houses with the staff in the basement, territorial preferences could be maintained. In the much smaller houses of middle-class Ireland, the proximity was such that it can hardly have been pleasant for either employer or employee.

There did not seem to be much sense of female solidarity in my mother's attitude to either the maids (a constant in her domestic life) or to women generally, other than her small number of intimate friends. The lengths to which she went to keep the world at bay extended to all her acquaintances and many of her intimates. That she might have had something to hide seems without foundation, other than the critical light in which she felt the world regarded her. No team player but an incorrigible individualist, she had already, when in her twenties, separated herself from the trammels of convention, while appearing superficially to be the soul of conservatism. Her revolution was internal, her laughter private: she hoped that nobody would notice but naturally they did, and marked her down as eccentric and peculiar. She adopted the stratagem of wearing large opaque Hollywood film-star sunglasses as a form of disguise and, at the first sign of summer, they were donned. Behind sunglasses, or a book, she was safe.

CHAPTER 6

To differentiate between my parents was always a question of texture and scent. My father, essentially a tweedy individual, was a man of coarse textures, military uniform or rough-hewn jackets, cavalry twill trousers, the pervasive smell of the pungent Camel cigarettes he habitually smoked. About him hung the aura of horsemanship and vigorous exercise and, although he had ceased to engage in either, they had left a mark on his presence and the way he moved.

Softer fabrics, the silks and poplins of summer dresses and headscarves, represented my mother; the sheer feel of demure outdoor wear. If the whiff of face powder and cosmetics arrayed before the mirrors of her dressing-table evoked some of the enigma of her personality, the motion and swish of certain dresses did so equally. That a small child should be affected by the allure of his mother's perfume may sound improbable, yet the sensation is one of pleasing identification with a particular person, rather than what an adult would consider to be sexual attraction.

I recognized from an early age that my mother, unlike the mothers of other children on the street, was not of the same world as them, or even possibly from the same species. Other children's mothers were more down-to-earth, direct in their language or abrupt in their treatment of their husbands and large families; hearty, matter-of-fact individuals, baking flour on their arms as they emerged from the kitchen, throwing their apron into a corner and pulling a packet of cigarettes from a cardigan pocket, lighting up with aplomb and puffing contentedly at the front door as they chatted nonchalantly with the postman. These characteristics in other women were infinitely intriguing to me in so far as they differed so totally from my mother's demeanour. In her daily life it was as though she were on stage, a character in some domestic theatre piece in which I played a small part, no more than as a minor extra, a third spear-carrier. She was the sole star of the play of which the story was unknown; one could get only an occasional glimpse of its meaning. The various roles she played— wife, mother, daughter, carer, *hausfrau*—seemed merely labels which identified her in some moments of the day; the true elusive person could be imagined or understood only through the ethereal scent of her perfume or the almost inaudible sensation of her dress fabric as it was rucked, its folds falling together or laid out on a couch like the smooth contours of a hillside.

In all the things of the physical and public world in which my father excelled, my mother exhibited neither interest nor accomplishment. She dressed fashionably in the Sybil Connolly manner, read modern English or American novelists: Priestley, Waugh, Huxley, A.J. Cronin, Maugham, Thornton Wilder and Hemingway. She gardened, cared for her family, supervised the maid. She would, if asked to define herself, probably have put 'wife' as her first qualification, although she was educated, intelligent and with an incisive and critically astute mind, and might have, if she had not married, had a career – lecturer in the Department of Words at the Royal Quotation University. A natural reticence and profound sense of doubt would have prevented her from ever becoming a pedant. She had inherited her concept of life and the married state uncritically from her parents, whose sense of Victorian decorum made the world a place of predictable rhythms. The husband operated in the public domain, the wife in the domestic. For my mother, this definition sufficed to explain the necessary world.

Her interest in etymology was such that she might be found motionless in the garden, secateurs in hand, or in the middle of some domestic task, transfixed by the contemplation of an interesting word. Her reading brought her great pleasure—it was the chief stimulus of her life—and the words she seized upon, often the most commonplace, were a source of infinite speculation and delight.

'Yokel—now that's an interesting word. I wonder what its origins are?' And she would be off, burrowing in the dictionary, considering the possibilities, recollecting its use in current novels or in her past reading.

'*A rustic, a country bumpkin*, yes that's correct, but from what?'

'*Possibly from English dialect yokel, meaning "green woodpecker"*.' This she could not accept without further verification.

'*An offensive term for a country dweller, regarded as lacking in sophistication, education or other qualities thought typical of city dwellers*.' Then she came to the entry she had been expecting, '*Origin uncertain. Ah ha!*' The dictionary had failed again; they had no idea, so they just made it up. She was amused by the image of celebrated Oxford scholars just chancing their collective and finely veined arms. From 'origin uncertain', she proceeded to develop her own etymological path, always more convoluted than the terse telegramese of the dictionary. It normally began with a 'what if...'.

'What if the word is not English at all but from some other language, an Anglicization of some foreign...some Gaelic word? English dictionaries are very weak on the subject of Irish etymologies.' She paused for thought and gave '*Eochaill!*'

'Imagine this scene: Sir Walter Raleigh, fresh from his victories in the Americas and Ireland, a successful participant in the plantation of Munster, returns to England with a group of his Irish retainers, kerns in fact. The gentlemen at court enquire where he came upon such raw and hairy rustics?'

"*Eochaill*" he replies, "from my broad and well-watered meadolandes in Corke where I have but recently builded me a fine gabled house." The gentlemen are amused.'

"Eochaills are they, a more succinct term than our country bumpkin; we like it mightily."

So the place-name of his town in Ireland, now Anglicized as Youghal, gives to English the term yokel for a country bumpkin.' She is pleased with her proposed derivation. 'Better than green woodpeckers. More plausible certainly.'

Despite their divergence in character and interests, in sentiment both my parents were similar. They were deeply imbued with the post-colonial world view in which their tastes had been formed and by the tail-end of British rule in Ireland, as indelibly as any Brahmin couple in New Delhi were formed by the remnants of the Raj. Despite their shared nationalist backgrounds, hers cultural and pacifist, his physical force, they had little esteem for any concept of a Gaelic Ireland. Traditional Irish music and Gaelic games were neither heard of nor mentioned in Windermere and I remained unaware of their existence for many years. Urban in their upbringing, the wider world held my parents' attention, the four green fields and dancing at the crossroads as foreign to them as the rituals of Kalahari nomads.

CHAPTER 7

My early childhood was spent during World War II, and while the war imposed little damage on neutral Éire, other than the allegedly accidental bombings of Dublin and Wexford, as the national topic of conversation it became a constant. The war affected the life of the population at large in a manner graded in terms of their inconvenience—which products one could or could not procure—and a proscription on travel other than to Britain. In our home the war was a vivid and intimate presence. My father, as a career officer in the Irish Defence Forces, was stationed in Cork and our family lives were entwined with the doings of the military and the invisible war. Visitors to our home, other than my mother's family and friends, were almost entirely his brother officers and their wives.

The smell of polished leather was pervasive: highly buffed shoes, Sam Browne belts, shoulder straps. Gloriously burnished riding boots were worn for formal occasions. The polishing was the duty of my father's batman, Sergeant Bates, or the task fell to Annie, who regarded it as a sacred duty on which the family's honour depended, rather than as an onerous chore. Being an impeccably turned-out officer was a cult of those non-combatant times; well-ironed uniforms, brightly glowing leather, polished brass buttons and insignia were *de rigueur*. The house reeked of the strange indefinable odour of the fabric from which the military uniforms were cut, fibrous and tangy. The army was on permanent military alert in case the European war should change in some manner which directly affected Éire's interests. Invasion by one belligerent or another was believed to be a constant threat—by the Germans as a land-bridge for an offensive against Britain, by the British (and this in tacit agreement with the Irish government) as a last ditch retreat for the British Army to hold out against Germany.

As though my father were a hussar in the Austro-Hungarian cavalry, all the archaic trappings of military manners were still maintained in the new Irish Army, which was less than twenty years old when I was born. Against the side of the wardrobe of my parents' bedroom rested his cavalry swords, their polished steel blades engraved in Celtic interlace; the leather-scabbarded one with its brass handguard was for drill use, the shiny chromium-plated one with the silver-plated handguard for dress wear—the only photograph in which the latter appears is of my parents' wedding, with my father dressed in his regimentals and evidently prepared for operatic valour on the stage of La Scala. This epauletted and silver-braided costume seems like fancy dress, the world of Sigmund Romberg and *The Student Prince*, yet from the perspective of the early nineteen forties, active horse cavalry was a quite recent memory. The last cavalry charge on a European battlefield took place towards the end of World War I, in 1917 in Belgium, when my father was sixteen years old.

My father's hair was so black, it looked dyed. His ritual of hair preparation was as precise as everything else he did, quickly, efficiently and, if the process had been timed and filmed, he doubtless took exactly the same number of minutes to shave and to comb his hair every morning, and used identical gestures. The hair was an important aspect of the military man, a finishing touch like the polished boots and the gleaming buttons. Into each palm he placed a small deposit of hair cream, rubbed the palms together, then applied his hands to his hair, rucking it into a spiky mass (which would become the acme of young men's fashion some sixty years later), then combing it back smoothly into a lacquered caul-like headpiece. From his hair down, he paid precisely similar attention to his appearance and would have merged seamlessly into a wartime Humphrey Bogart film as an officer from central casting. In fact, he was a man of impeccable black and white provenance, his cigarette held in a long ebony holder, letting the smoke waft languidly around him, occasionally blowing a smoke ring as though to insert a punctuation mark in an anecdote. Throughout my childhood I watched my father's rituals closely since they seemed to establish some indisputable norm of behaviour, the precise meaning of which I could never grasp. It was his synchronized methodology that I found fascinating and compelling. I wondered how he always remembered to do things in the same precisely choreographed process, never guessing that he did not have to think about it at all and that he acted from ingrained habit. Everything about my father which was different from my mother's manners was of interest to me, and their individual identification with smells, tones and textures was a veritable education in sensuous and tactile sensations. I felt that if I understood why they were so different, then I would know their secret, the bond between them, which excluded children and gave them an indivisible unity. I never did discover their secret, if indeed there was one to be revealed.

The comings and goings of the military men, the click of their heels and the sharp tap of leather on the tiled floor of our hall set up a repertoire of sounds and smells which defines the time. We were witness to the great and tragic movements of contemporary history, yet apart from them, preserved from the threat of death or destruction by being a small island nation, neutral, insignificant, and fortunately, on the dark edge of Europe, very far from the horrors of Stalingrad and the Eastern Front.

Yet there was a sense of Balkan self-importance in the air, a small impoverished country on the fringes of great events, lustily whistling past the graveyard and parading the cardboard might of half a million men in uniform, equipped with little more than token arms to oppose the invader. Conversations amongst the officers often concentrated on how long (and to what purpose other than honour) the army might hold back the advance of a combat-hardened invading Panzer division as it lumbered up the beach at Ballybunion, while the dug-in Irish forces were being strafed by the Luftwaffe. Half an hour? A day? A week? Indefinitely? The younger the officer, the more optimistic their projections. My father, well-read in tactics and military history, as well as being an attentive observer of the current conflict, quoted Napoleon and von Clausewitz. A realist, he had no expectation that the Nazi sweep across Continental Europe could be halted by a poorly equipped force, lacking in combat experience.

As the senior officer amongst his group of friends, my father held precedence because of rank, age and by force of his ready wit and dominant personality. When young, he had all the attributes for a promising military career: he was handsome, efficient, a good horseman, a crack shot, allied to an impeccable nationalist background and had, while still a teenager, served in the IRA against the Black and Tans during the War of Independence. He was cultured, affable and well liked in the officers' mess. He brought an atmosphere of confidence, well-being and can-do-ness into our family life. During the war, when he wanted a wide-angle attachment for his Zeiss-Ikon camera and was unable to import one, he made it himself from solid brass on his lathe, had it chromium-plated, and used it as an attachment for his precision camera, itself a triumph of Swiss engineering. My father belonged to a world of possibilities. A champion swimmer and golfer, he regarded his sporting accomplishments as mere recreation, activities he might engage in or not, as the humour took him; the competitive aspect was to him utterly unimportant. He loved opera, the literature of exploration and military history, yet hardly read a novel in his life, the real and the tangible being his world.

My father's officer friends were large Falstaffian figures, good-humoured, ever ready for a joke. They were invigorated by their military activities, in a state of perpetual motion, setting off at odd hours with my father for distant places on army business. War was the constant topic of conversation amongst them, the prospect of the combatants interminably agonized over, the movements of the Allied and Axis powers, derived from military briefings, analysed to infinity. There was a sense of being under siege, and my father, well travelled in continental Europe, expressed the commonly held view in the Ireland of the day that the country had to become self-sufficient. This invariably led to the proposal of hare-brained schemes for the manufacture of everything from bathtub-gin to turf-powered submarines. In the void created by the absence of actual hostilities, fantasy was never far from the surface in these discussions.

Our dog Blitz seemed also to symbolize the war and he was devoted to my father's comings and goings, beginning to bark when he heard the distinctive sound of the army transport bringing my father home, even though it was still a few streets away. Our own car remained for the duration of the war up on blocks in the garage, looking like a caged creature, impotent and abandoned. When the officers were visiting, they occupied the drawing room with their large forms, standing by the mantelpiece, declaiming the latest analysis of battle strategy, quoting examples from earlier engagements, assessing the strength of respective forces, reserves, armaments, resources, supply-lines, strategic intentions. They were loud, large and given to practical jokes. Music always seemed to accompany these gatherings—the chorus of the Hebrew Slaves from *Nabucco* or John McCormack on the gramophone. But Lalle Andersen on the radio with her rendition of 'Lilli Marlene' in German was capable of stopping all conversation as the anthem of the war years expressed exactly the tension and *longueurs* of the times. They listened with pleasure to Marlene Dietrich's English language version, but with rapture when the broadcast was in German, as though this even more closely evoked the alienation of war.

The 'officers' mess' was in session at Windermere, and the living room was a throng of loud men and their shriller wives. My mother's quip on the departure of their friends on a previous occasion—'The tumult and the shouting dies; The Captains and *their Queens* depart:'—had set a style to these laughter-laden social occasions. Quotations and literary allusions were part of the fashionable currency of the time, and in these my mother excelled, never at a loss when a Shakespearean tag would fit the moment. For one to whom the cult of vagueness seemed habitual, she could be razor sharp when her mind was engaged.

The men were all captains in rank, while my father was already a commandant. Many had entered the army at the beginning of the Emergency, the Irish euphemism for World War II, when there had been a sudden rapid enlistment of officers and men, creating a substantial force for the defence of the nation, even if it was ill-equipped and initially untrained. Alcohol at Windermere was served in moderation since both my parents were temperate drinkers. The products of my mother's baking skills circulated, prepared in the afternoon with Annie's assistance. Sponge and fruit cakes, elaborately sculpted tarts and exotic cupcakes on ornate two- and three-tier stands, sandwiches on long Victorian china dishes, were arrayed on small tables around the room. Their regimental group photographs establish the appearance and identities of the captains: seated in serried rows flanking their commanding officer, all in riding boots, some with riding crop in hand, cavalry men, half-centaurs in bulls-wool and Brasso, as dashing and as loyal as any army could desire.

CHAPTER 8

'The aunt', as well as being a genuine biological and genetic aunt, my mother's elder sister, derived her facetious nickname from an overbearing character in the popular literature of the time. In the comic novels of P.G. Wodehouse, their well-meaning but ineffectual hero Bertie Wooster's estimate of his Aunt Agatha (alleged by Bertie to eat nails) was of a woman firmly in the mould of Wilde's Lady Bracknell. Neither Aunt Agatha, Lady B., nor indeed the aunt suffered fools and, in their more challenged moments all may well have eaten nails. If the aunt had a self-appointed mission in life, it was to puncture what she perceived to be the pretensions of others. Frequently her victims were quite without pretensions, and were unaware that they were registering highly on her personal Richter scale of social defectiveness, or outraging her private norms of etiquette. Further aspects of her mission to the world was the exposure of ignorance, foolishness and ill-breeding, the last-mentioned category a portmanteau encompassing every manner of behaviour which irritated her. A Don Quixote to the *bourgeoisie*, she raised her lance against all who lacked appropriate

humility. On a stifling afternoon during a previous summer when my
mother was due to meet the aunt in town, she stopped to get ice-cream
cones for my brother and me. The aunt appeared at the meeting-place
but, on seeing us, just walked past in stony silence, disappearing down
a side street. My mother was abashed at having been ignored, but in a
conflict she was always prepared to absorb the blame; she wondered if
her sister's sight could be failing, or was she suffering from a sudden
attack of amnesia? When they met at Rosenheim the following day,
the aunt was vehement in her denunciation of our faulty upbringing.

'Your children were eating ice-cream cones', she hissed like an
enraged python about to strike. 'Only shop-girls eat in the street!'

If the aunt was avowedly not a feminist, on the Groucho Marx
principle of not wishing to be counted amongst any elite who would
have accepted her as a member, she was in some respects a feminist in
chains, embattled against a humiliatingly unjust world in which men
(and colluding women) stifled female talent. As a teacher of teenagers,
she passionately believed in the intellectual potential of young girls,
and devoted her life to fostering what they might achieve. Dismissing
the concept of the supposed frailty of women, she vacillated between
her firm conviction that young girls would benefit by being exposed
to the highest academic standards, yet held the converse belief that
the majority of adult women were not worth much consideration in
general, and none of hers personally.

Competitive from her schooldays, she belonged more amongst
those nineteenth-century women like Florence Nightingale, who
pulled against the traces of abnormally restrictive conventions, than
in an era when women's opportunities were becoming less rigidly
defined. She thought of herself as being as good as anybody, better
than most, and prepared to do battle with those who were unfortunate
to cross her path or opposed her in any way.

The aunt's school and college photographs show her in fiercely sporty
mode, a team player in every activity then available to women—tennis,

golf, hockey and swimming. In each group she sits resolutely glaring at the photographer with an expression of fierce no-surrender. The hockey team photographs show an Amazon with feral glare, ready to thwart any opposition with a poke of her stick. Whatever the success record may have been of the teams to which she belonged, they do not look like easy quitters. This was the school and college environment to which she gravitated, the tough camaraderie of contact sports and the competitive attraction of the most physical and combative activities considered acceptable for female participation—in an era when regulations at University College Cork forbade women students from sitting on the grass in the quadrangle—it was considered improper.

The aunt had by the mid-century preserved the archaic appearance of a flapper of the nineteen twenties, the era during which her dress sense had solidified, although she had hardly flapped much when of an age to do so. She was severe, schoolmarmish, disapproving of all and sundry in both her family's houses in Cork. Nothing came up to her self-ordained high standards of behaviour, by which her sister, as resident carer for their mother, was constantly falling below acceptable objectives. Nature, when handing out gifts of character, had been liberal to the aunt in granting her an excess of self-confidence, as well as a God-given certainty that her personal opinions were of greater merit than those of anybody to whom she might be speaking. With such gifts of courage and self-regard, a small but significant matter had been omitted from her formidable makeup: she was afraid of animals. More precisely, the entirety of the animal kingdom displeased and unnerved her. Horses and dogs, cows (every humble one of which she assumed to be a bull), sheep, she found them all frightening. When walking alone along a country road, if she encountered a stray donkey grazing unconcernedly on the grassy verge, she would instantly reverse her path or take a five-mile detour via by-roads, in order not to have to pass the beast. Her distaste for all four-legged creatures frequently caused her inconvenience, yet she was forthright enough to be dismissive of there being a problem.

If four legs were bad, more than four necessitated an evacuation of the premises. With creepy-crawlies, the aunt lost all resolve. The sight of any many-legged insect—a cockroach, woodlouse, centipede or other scurrying mite—was calculated to make her, a person who otherwise admitted to no human weaknesses, feel ill. The appearance of a spider was enough to cause her to don her hat and coat and leave the house. This was the sole facet of her life in which she grudgingly might admit that the male person had some function in the world, since men seemed impervious to arachnophobia or other negative thoughts regarding the creatures that lurked in cupboards and in the damp places of houses.

Whether on account of the advent of modern pesticides, nuclear-strength household detergents, central-heating, or some natural decline in their numbers, the insects that infested all houses during my childhood—flies, majestically large bluebottles, legions of ants, cockroaches, nests of spiders, silverfish, and other creatures—are now less frequently encountered. What I found of absorbing interest as just another strange manifestation of the natural world, the aunt dreaded, and instead of doing battle with ammonia against the creepy-crawlies which moved on the face of the earth, she capitulated instantly to the threats of the insect world. The darkness of Rosenheim made its more hidden spaces attractive to the scurrying and darting fraternity, and any visit there for the aunt could be guaranteed to produce a face-to-face encounter between herself and the swiftly moving inhabitant of the sculleries, confrontations in which the many-legged ones usually triumphed. She called on Mrs Luby to deal summarily with the interlopers.

It was the aunt's firm conviction that the Plagues of Egypt numbered far more than the statutory nine: she believed them to be limitless, and that they had been contrived to make her personal life uncomfortable and travelling to distant places hazardous. To my mother, the aunt alone constituted all the plagues together, and she would sink into a couch in despair when a visit from the aunt was announced by letter, reclining

Ophelia-like with the offending note fluttering from her fingers. In later years, the announcement of an impending visit led her to more personally depressing recollections of the day of Grandmother's death and the aunt's contribution to making it as memorable as a day of doom. Then she would hold her head in her hands and weep, but the cause of this particular distress, to which I was an unknowing participant, was not for many years explained.

The aunt's self-appointed role as the scourge of her family concealed a deeper malaise: her unresolved bitterness towards her late father, which fuelled a life-long disdain for all men. In an act of savage destruction, she used the occasion of my grandmother's death, which occurred when I was nine years old, to deliver the coup de grâce to her father's memory in a manner that weighed on her conscience for the remainder of her life.

CHAPTER 9

My father seldom spoke of his youth, his parents or of his six siblings. Neither did he often mention his political activities during the War of Independence which directly followed his schooldays, and before he had joined the Defence Forces in 1922. He seemed disassociated from republican or nationalist politics, his involvement being with the State and its armed forces. However, he would occasionally narrate incidents from those revolutionary years to my brother and me.

Two stories remain in my memory, attractive for their sense of boy-scout adventure rather than for any political content. One concerns an incident where he and a fellow IRA volunteer were in some remote cottage outside Kilkenny city where my father's family lived. The two volunteers were engaged in bomb-making or the manufacturing of explosives. Foolhardy, and indifferent to danger in the way of young men since long before the Siege of Troy, his companion was smoking a cigarette. They both knew that their superior officers had repeatedly warned them about the capacity of explosives to detonate at the slightest provocation. Either my father's friend dropped his cigarette into the incendiary mix, or a spark from it caused an ignition: the material they were working on suddenly exploded and the other man received serious injuries. My father had brought this volunteer to the secret location in the sidecar of his motorcycle, and managed to get the injured man back into the sidecar. They then went for help to the home of some discreet nationalist doctor in the area.

I was often impressed by the presence on the inside of my father's left arm of a livid scar, running from his wrist to his armpit, where he had been burned by the blast, yet he had managed to ride his motorbike for assistance. The veracity of this anecdote is not helped by my father's propensity to make fun of his exploits and sometimes to claim that he had got the scar in totally unpolitical circumstances. These included jumping from the window of a house while fleeing from the wrath of the father of a girl he had been visiting or, in a further version, the wound was received while rescuing a terrified young woman from a blazing building. In all these tall tales, he consciously maintained the role of unreliable witness. He also attributed his thinning hair to having scraped his head during some similar amorous exploit, while descending on a rope ladder from a tryst with a love-struck lady. His tales were delivered with such conviction that, while he was narrating an adventure, even the most preposterous claims seemed plausible.

Another one of his derring-do tales concerned a night-time raid on a Royal Irish Constabulary police barracks (a commonplace enough IRA activity during the period) which sounds more like a comic escapade from a silent movie than an incident in the deadly struggle that was taking place at the time. The barracks in question was well stocked with arms. The revolutionaries needed the guns to supply the local brigade, which was not having much luck in holding on to its arms, living as it was under a state of martial law, with frequent raids and curfews. The munitions were kept in an upstairs room at the rear of the barracks, the windows of which were heavily barred.

A diversion, guaranteed to last a considerable time, was organized to occupy the small RIC garrison in the public room of the barracks. All the officers were long-time residents of the area, well known to local people and not opposed to sharing a convivial drink with a neighbour, even during perilous times. The diversion involved some plausible benefactor calling to the RIC barracks, with a few bottles of poitín as token payment for a summons. Hospitality demanded that the illicit alcohol be sampled. While drinks were being offered in the front of the barracks, and the men of the garrison were getting drunk, the IRA team, of which my father was the junior member, had backed a lorry up to the rear of the building, erected a ladder to the window, and proceeded to saw through the bars. All this activity sounds as if it would have taken many hours to accomplish, and with the noise of sawing unlikely not to be heard by the men who were supposed to be guarding their armoury. Nonetheless, the raid succeeded; the IRA men removed the bars, got in the window, and emptied the room of its stock of rifles and ammunition. By this point, the members of the garrison, according to my father, were blissfully spreadeagled on the floor of their quarters, having succumbed to the power of the poitín, while the raiders successfully escaped with their haul.

These and other stories of his adventures were occasionally produced, usually by way of entertainment if my brother or I were confined to bed with a cold. I never got the impression that they represented a 'My Fight for Irish Freedom' syndrome of egotistical narrative, since they were always depicted as madcap scrapes, carried out in an atmosphere of youthful bravado, rather than as acts of war upon a dangerous enemy. He told us about these adventures as though they had just been the high-spirited events in his youth, and indeed, perhaps that is exactly what they were. Somewhere between his dramatic accounts of escaping on a rope-ladder from a burning building, a terrified young woman clasped to his chest, and engaging in illegal political activity that might end in death, lay the reality of his experiences, satirized perhaps as a protection against thinking too deeply about what he had been experienced, and its cost in lives. As a corrective to the fatuous tales of damsels in distress, his Óglaigh na hÉireann membership card for 1919, when he was eighteen years old, was found amongst his papers at his death.

CHAPTER 10

A different type of gathering took place independently of the social evenings at Windermere and at peculiar hours, when a smaller number of the captains, minus their queens, gathered to listen to wartime news broadcasts on our high frequency radio, and to hear, when they could, the broadcasts from the *Reichsrundfunk* in Berlin. The very English voice of William Joyce, Lord Haw-Haw, the more familiar-sounding Francis Stuart, and various other unidentified voices were listened to in absolute silence. If I was allowed into the room, I was enjoined not to utter a sound. These broadcasts generated intense speculation, although the reception was sometimes faint or sufficiently intermittent that had the listeners not had subsequent access to the logged monitoring transcripts acquired through G2, the Irish military intelligence bureau, it is unlikely that the officers, on some occasions, would have appreciated more than the gist of the broadcasts. The sheer effrontery of Allied or Irish citizens broadcasting for the Nazis clearly held a fascination for my father's group of friends. While they were not sympathetic to what was clearly German propaganda, and were, from a military perspective, entirely supportive of the Allied, principally British, war effort, the broadcasts succeeded in causing a frisson of unease. The sense of certainty which they projected – the inevitability of an Axis victory, the new world order, the unquestioned virtue of the German cause and the supreme wisdom of the Führer in all things— had a hypnotic effect on the listeners. Yet when the broadcasts were over, my father and his cronies still laughed, as when Stuart compared Hitler to Parnell, and often broke into the words of a popular contemporary satirical song heard on the BBC:

> *Lord Haw-Haw, the humbug of Hamburg,*
> *The rollicking rake of the Reich.*

The radio was a principal household god and it sat supreme and opulent beside my father's armchair in the drawing room, its polished wooden casing and many dials and controls forbidden to my clumsy and childish hands. While I recollect the excitement of the gatherings and the broadcasts, my understanding of their relevance is entirely retrospective. Something important was being broadcast, but as to what it was, I had no comprehension whatsoever beyond that it was 'news', the information that came out of the radio, and that it was about the war, an event which was as ubiquitous as it was inexplicable. Nonetheless, this sort of incident served to tie in the focus of our lives to the faraway war and I was aware of the existence of Berlin, Dresden, London and Coventry long before I had absorbed the presence of Bandon or Midleton, country towns in the immediate vicinity of the city. The ethereal and crackling faraway voice of those broadcasts from Berlin was also a topic of dispute amongst the captains, some of whom were what would have been called 'West Brits', strongly pro-British, while others were of more republican stripe, and inclined to suggest that such broadcasts were British counter-propaganda designed to flush out sources of potential dissent and collaborators at home. However, none of the listeners seriously entertained the latter proposal.

My father performed on the radio (or wireless as he habitually called it) as other musicians did on the concert hall stage. Although his repertoire was unlimited, his audience was small, confined to two credulous children and a few conspiratorial adults. His performances, which must have taken place only when my brother and I were young enough, around six and seven, and sufficiently technologically unaware, as to be easily deluded by his sleight of hand, were characteristic of his indulgence in private jokes. These might be directed, without discrimination, at any adult, child or stranger. His concert programme was the *Radio Times*, which gave all the BBC programme schedules, and the *Cork Examiner* for their Irish equivalents. He would announce, as though he were a master of ceremonies, that some particular signal such as the station call-sign or specific music was about to be performed.

He might begin, 'In three seconds the wireless will play Holst's "The Planets"' and, according to cue, a brittle radio voice would announce, 'The Royal Liverpool Philharmonic Orchestra under the baton of Sir Malcolm Sargent will now play for you "The Planets" suite by Gustav Holst', and so it would begin. I never failed to be impressed by my father's capacity to extract from the radio exactly what he required and assumed that he had some electronic mastery over the contents of the box, and that whatever was broadcast in other houses was entirely different.

'And now we shall have the news from Broadcasting House and the sound of Big Ben', and there it would be, bonging loudly following my father's flourish of his wrist in the direction of the radio, drawing out of it anything he pleased. Possessed of an inscrutable poker face, he was capable of engaging in sustained jokes or subterfuges, which he would pursue as long as his audience was prepared to believe in him. If eventually caught out, or tiring of the matter, he would laugh and say that it was a good joke and we should be wary of being duped. But, repeatedly, my brother and I fell for his ruses, lulled by his confident and authoritative commands to the radio to perform.

He also liked to conduct the orchestral performances on the radio, standing in front of the drawing-room fire with a pencil or one of my mother's knitting needles as his baton. I had never seen a live orchestra, although I was familiar with their appearance from the encyclopaedia photographs, and the arrangement of the musicians on stage had been explained to me. When my father conducted Beethoven's Ninth Symphony, it was as though the entire performance hung entirely on his every gesture, cajoling the strings, enticing the timpani, drawing in the soloists with imperious gestures. It appeared that from a family drawing room in suburban Cork, isolated on the perimeter of the European carnage, one of the world's great orchestras was being directed. While he conducted, my mother would be absorbed in her reading, occasionally glancing up with a half-amused smile, my brother and I the rapt audience, awaiting his precise and eloquent gestures as he led the orchestra through the work's movements.

As he got older, my father's complexion darkened and his hair grew thinner, so that his face and forehead assumed a richly tanned and polished look, accentuating the hazel colour of his eyes. His appearance, when he was dressed in his tweedy civilian clothes, frequently led to him being taken for a foreigner or a tourist. While he possibly did not court this image, the fact that he always carried his obviously foreign-looking and expensive camera on its polished strap over his shoulder made him look like a man with a purpose other than merely strolling down the street. In later years he carried his camera about with him without ever apparently taking a photograph; I wonder whether it even contained film? This camera-toting in a world that hardly aspired beyond the level of the Box Brownie, and it only brought out for holiday snaps and weddings, made some statement with which he evidently identified, a means of being other in some way. But to what purpose? The camera was one signature; a cigarette in a long holder was another, habitual tweeds a third. The purpose of the holder cannot have been to protect his skin from nicotine, because the fingers of his right hand were heavily stained a rich yellow ochre. Was it simply establishing an image? This seems improbable, yet nothing else suggests itself beyond the pleasure of smoking through a long holder which gave the smoke a coolness and heightened the sensation.

The conclusion of the war in 1945 appeared to drag out in a lengthy sequel as though its aftermath had a continuing if undramatic influence on my family life. But the sense of urgency and the camaraderie disappeared, the captains finally departed as the army demobilized its considerable manpower, inducted for the duration of the conflict. The clichéd and blackly comic question voiced by British ex-servicemen in post-war films and in many print contexts, 'Did you have a good war, old chap?', as though World War II had been some kind of sustained blood sport, riding to hounds or drag-hunting on the banks of the Rhine, has its application in Éire too. My father did have a good war and was not encouraged by the anticlimax that followed it.

CHAPTER 11

The maid's room occupied one side of the landing next to Grandmother's at the top of the house. From here to the kitchen was a series of descents by little flights and levels like the arrangement of a baroque landscape garden inserted into a modest terrace house. Mary Mary never left the door of her room open, but I became adept at kneeling and peering through the keyhole. The interior of her bedroom would have astonished Grandmother if she had any idea of the rococo splendours of the interior. Mary Mary was religious to a point that she had created in her room a shrine of Latin American splendour, undetected by her bedridden employer, whose poor sense of smell had not alerted her to the full beauty of Mary Mary's exoticism. Mary Mary was a fanatical devotee, and the interior of her room, viewed through the constricting lens of the keyhole, was a brilliant theatre of candlelight, crowded with night-lights and candles, filling the small room with a close approximation of one-hundred candle power, in contrast to the dim twenty watt bulbs in the rest of the house. Rosenheim was lit sparingly in the manner of the era when electricity first became available locally, and before it was the norm to brightly illumine domestic interiors.

When Mary Mary was not engaged in her tasks—cleaning, carrying buckets of coal upstairs to tend Grandmother's fire or running errands for Mrs Luby—she disappeared to her room and lit another candle. They burned permanently, even as she slept, when her recumbent form surrounded by a bower of candlelight must have given the scene the look of a virgin-martyr's cult-shrine in some Iberian pilgrimage church: 'Blessed Mary Mary of Rosenheim, patron of the damp souls of housemaids'. In the adjoining room her stern employer lay similarly recumbent, as in a barely lit anteroom to the unacknowledged and unsuspected shrine of the blessed one. To Grandmother, any overt display of religious sentiment was a manifestation of what she disparaged as 'peasant superstition', a term of supreme derision, and she would have been deeply perturbed had she become aware of Mary Mary's passion. Knowledge of the practice of overt religiosity would have led to her immediate replacement.

The keyhole view was suddenly blocked and a voice came from within. 'Go away, boy, or I'll tell your gran that you was spying on me in me pelt. She doesn't like sneaks.'

Meekly I departed to see if Mrs Luby was cooking. Mary Mary followed me to the kitchen just in case I might comment on her fire-raising activities to Mrs Luby, and when I said nothing, cajoled the housekeeper into producing something for me to eat.

'The poor boy is starving, Mrs Luby. I'll make a pot of tea.'

We sat around the kitchen table while the housekeeper bustled, providing a buttered tea-brack or hot griddle-cakes with honey, distracted from polishing a pair of heavy brass candlesticks. She returned them to a cupboard. The following week the candlesticks would disappear from the house and provide a boost to Mrs Luby's modest wages as housekeeper to a dying woman, a pyromaniacal maid and a gullible child. Late in the evening, as I dozed at Mrs Luby's table, my mother or father would come to walk me home to Windermere.

Mrs Luby took snuff and liked to share it with her cronies when entertaining them in the kitchen. Mary Mary was frequently dispatched to one of the forbidden shops for replenishment of supplies, paid for out of the housekeeping money, or to get her out of the way while the old women shared scandal in the kitchen. Mary Mary was slightly plump and pretty in an unadorned manner, intensely innocent and utterly tactless, so the parish claques were happy to have her out of earshot for a while. The maid's absences provided me with an opportunity to inspect her room and to see the most recent additions. My parents would have been appalled had they even suspected the religious displays and sheer firepower behind the maid's firmly closed bedroom door, although it was curious that the pervasive stench of candle wax on the upper landing did not attract their attention. My mother's opinion would have matched her own mother's dictum; my father's agnosticism would have been both more vocal and more vitriolic on the subject.

Table, wardrobe, bedside table, shelves, all surfaces in the room were decked out as shrines to Mary Mary's innumerable and increasingly more populous dramatis personae. She added a saint a week, a blessed, a venerable or others of more obscure status as holy persons of whom she had got a picture, card, statuette or some curious little bound fabric package the size of a postage stamp, with a saint's name embroidered on the outside. With a commendable sense of display, using cardboard boxes and packaging of various sizes and paper doilies for effect, she arranged each major shrine and sub-shrine at many levels, with the image of the holy one on top; each level, annex, and addition to the shrines provided a place for further votive lights. The dressing table and wardrobe mirrors reflected the candle flames, and the scene was repeated ad infinitum, adding a dimension of depth and greatly magnifying the intensity and the brightness of the illuminations. I tiptoed around, examining each separate icon, the continued maintenance of which was consuming all the maid's earnings. The atmosphere in the small room was overpoweringly intense: a combination of burning candles, reflected light, the smell of wax and the heat generated in a confined space. Mary Mary's room was suffocating, its thermal rating far beyond the capacity even of the kitchen range. Hearing her key in the front door, I slipped out and entered Grandmother's room. She was sitting up and she stared at me accusingly.

'Where have you been, boy?'

'Oh, downstairs with Mrs Luby. She is chatting to Mrs Prunty.'

Grandmother raised an eyebrow at the mention of Mrs Prunty, another grizzled veteran of the housekeeper fraternity, but did not question me further.

Mary Mary was a replacement for Mary Street (who had come following the abrupt dismissal of Mary Brigid, on what grounds I had been unable to discover) and was about the same age, under twenty, as all the maids seemed to be to my untutored eye, like Pliny's observation on the crowds upon the Appian Way, 'always in or around about eighteen years of age'. Mary Street had been pretty in a decidedly contrived way and quite unfamiliar with any concept of truth. She lied to Grandmother, to Mrs Luby, to my parents, and even to me. I was the only person who always believed everything she said. Mary Street was interested in men, young men specifically, but any man was a topic of absorbing interest. She would invite me to come to the upstairs windows with her, or even into the front garden, ostensibly to pick roses for Grandmother's dressing table bouquet, in order to look at any promising male who was passing down the street; even the shell-shocked interested her and she had a sympathetic interest in any type of deformity. Perpetually in pursuit, her time was given over to discussing men, having assignations with them, and condemning them afterwards. Every time some potential admirer disappointed her, she resolved to have nothing further to do with men, until she was returning from the shops and encountered a strange barrowboy or deliveryman. In an instant she was smitten and ready for further romance. It was Mary Street who explained to me that Mr Daly had been in the trenches at Gallipoli and had lost his limbs when a fellow soldier with the Royal Munster Fusiliers had become deranged during a heavy Turkish bombardment and had blown himself up with his own hand grenade, inadvertently taking Mr Daly's arm and leg with him. My mother would never have imparted this succinct and gory image, but merely told me that it was rude to stare and placed an embargo on my pocket money until I was better behaved.

The maid lived permanently in the house, so that Grandmother should not be left on her own at night, and Mrs Luby went home to the buildings, as I did to Windermere. This neat arrangement left Mary Street free to entertain her men friends at leisure, between the bell ringing from upstairs and other domestic duties which Mrs Luby had itemized to occupy her time. The housekeeper became suspicious when an unexplained man's hat appeared on the hatstand in the hall and Mary Street was reported to my parents and threatened with dismissal. Mrs Luby did not wish for any scrutiny of what was for her a convenient and profitable position requiring minimum effort, although not advantageous in the purely salaried sense. Nonetheless, Mary Street concocted an explanation: her brother/father/nephew had called because there was an emergency at home, a sudden illness, and had left his hat behind. The story was not believed, but maids prepared to live-in and look after an elderly and bedridden old woman were not so easy to replace. Mary Street was (between assignations) hardworking, so she remained in her post despite the subsequent discovery of further items of male clothing, with similar 'family visits' provided as explanation.

Mary Street liked to maintain as many separate liaisons as her afternoon off and evening hours could accommodate. The idea of loyalty or dedication to a single admirer was foreign to her. If a few young men could be simultaneously juggled as rivals for her affections, then this greatly added to their interest. Gradually, aware that she was not under threat of instant dismissal, she enlisted Mrs Luby's assistance, and mine, in arranging her complex love life. If some young man, then out of favour, called during the day to arrange a meeting on her off-hours, Mrs Luby was to say that Mary Street did not work there any more. If my parents asked me if she had any visitors, I was bribed to remain mute with promises of a visit to one of the off-limits shops. Had my parents been more alert, my reticence should have informed them of the rich social life in the Rosenheim equivalent of Nighttown. That there might be jealousy between the maid's lovers added spice to their attentions and she exploited the mutual distaste of the rivals for each other and that Jim and Danny had had a fight on her account was a thrilling occurrence which she related with gasps and exclamations. She was not, of course, aware of the lengths to which these rivals might go in response to having their attentions played with.

Grandmother lay in her room, occasionally ringing one of her hand-bells. I played with the old radio and looked at the pictures in the art magazines from the eighteen nineties when Grandfather was a student at the Royal College of Art in London and women in the pictures wore floor-length dresses and carried feathered fans. Mrs Luby sat at the kitchen table carefully repairing a Spode ceramic soup tureen which would later appear in one of the city centre's antique shops, while Mary Street scrubbed the floor tiles in the hall, musing on whether she had invited Tom or Freddie to call (not both, she hoped) when the housekeeper and the boy had gone home.

Much later in the evening, after I had been taken home and was long in bed, a knock came to the Windermere hall door at an improbable hour for visitors. It was a policeman. Following some inaudible conversation, my mother, my brother and I, for my father was away on military manoeuvres, and Annie visiting her family in the country, walked over under the streetlights to Rosenheim. Alarmingly, there was another policeman on duty at the door and the house was unexpectedly crowded with strangers, although, to my disappointment, none of them appeared to be Mary Street's young men. I was intensely curious to see whether it was Tom or Freddie who had called. Even more improbably, Mrs Luby at this late hour was still on duty at her kitchen table dispensing tea to a crowd of chattering neighbours, who became silent and embarrassed when we entered.

Without a word, Mrs Luby took my mother's hand and led her upstairs as though to Grandmother's deathbed. My brother and I followed closely. We entered instead the maid's room. On the bed, fully clothed and with her arms by her side lay Mary Street, her head covered by a mass of matted bloodstained hair, her face white and inanimate. She was dead; hit over the head with a brick while out of the house in a nearby side street, on her way to a tryst and doubtless the victim of the jealousy of one of her admirers. My mother stared at her for a long time and then very gradually sank to the ground in a faint. Mrs Luby summoned some of the neighbours from downstairs and my mother was laid on a bed in another bedroom. So there were three recumbent women in adjoining rooms, one dead, another dying, the third in a state of extreme shock. We remained in Rosenheim that night and in the morning Mrs Luby was sent to the buildings in search of a replacement for the amorous Mary Street. On future occasions, rather more attention would be paid to the employees' references.

Within a few day of the demise of Mary Street, Mary Mary had been engaged. The latter came with a sheaf of solemn testimonials as to her pious nature and willingness to work unreasonable hours for little remuneration. In order to avoid confusion with her predecessor, my mother just added a second Mary to her actual name rather than having to use her real surname, which sounded similar to that of her late predecessor. The new recruit did not question this example of her employer's lofty wisdom and immediately answered to the name of Mary Mary. She was employed despite the fact that her religiosity did not appeal to my parents or to Mrs Luby, whose own religious views identified churchgoing as a source of gossip rather than spiritual renewal. To my parents, as to Grandmother, 'peasant beliefs' were not considered conducive to a proper working environment, but the new maid seemed respectful and competent in responding to instructions with a polite 'Yes'm' and 'No'm', and 'As you say'm, of course'm', and was the most promising of the candidates interviewed among the halt, the lame and the work-shy from the buildings.

Mary Street's personal belongings, consisting of her clothes and her lovers' letters, Mrs Luby committed to the kitchen range, the clothes as unfit to be worn by a respectable woman, the letters from admirers, which she read aloud to herself and subsequently, as examples of 'disgusting filth', quoted verbatim to her cronies. She had read them all with expressions of astonishment and interested outrage, dropping them page-by-page into the flaming maw of the firebox. My mother wrote a dutiful black-bordered letter of condolence to Mary Street's parents, who lived in the buildings, five minutes from Rosenheim. She did not visit their house, and their daughter was, in death, as divided from her employers as she had been in life.

Mary Mary and Mrs Luby seemed to represent the return of calm, although my mother's esteem for Mrs Luby, whom she had never rated very highly, dropped several notches on account of her failure to inform on Mary Street's interesting social life, now a topic of conversation to the entire neighbourhood. Women from the houses around Rosenheim were keen to enlighten my mother as to the fact that she had been harbouring a notorious libertine in her mother's house, always previously noted for its upright character and irreproachable respectability. Worse than the fact that what had been going on was visible to the neighbourhood was the relish with which the local nosy parkers recounted seeing Mary Street at large at night when she should have been indoors attending to the invalid. Neither Rosenheim nor Windermere had a telephone and it was understood that the maid should be trusted to attend to her duties. Not only did my mother feel complicit in Grandmother's neglect, she also felt responsible for Mary Street's welfare and believed that she had failed them both by being too trusting.

After this debacle and its grisly outcome, through all of which Grandmother either slept or rang her bells as the mood took her, it became imperative that she should be in the care of a more reliable person. Frequent references were made by my father, summoned from some distant region of the country to deal with the crisis, to the fact that 'the boy must have been aware of these goings on', to which my mother firmly assured him of my innocence and unawareness of worldly matters. The sight of the murdered maid had impressed me, more because I had never seen blood before except when I had bruised my knees, and I only vaguely understood its significance. Death I comprehended as something associated with Grandmother. That it should also apply to this young woman, full of life and keen for love and adventures, was not something I was able to focus on successfully. Mary Street had been hit over the head in the dark with a brick (when she should have been minding Grandmother). That she had been hurt by the incident was certainly comprehensible, but for her death and all the blood, for the violence and finality I had no framework. She had been fun, laughing and joking with Mrs Luby and with me, then she was gone and was not to be referred to again (except out of my hearing).

CHAPTER 12

Occasionally my grandmother's and my roles might be reversed, with her more appropriately becoming the carer, I the cared-for one. In general she was either too ill or too self-absorbed to notice that I, as a small boy, needed attention. Generally she did not direct her concern towards me, but regarded me as the audience for her monologues—a strictly one-way traffic—or as messenger boy to the kitchen. Of placid temperament, I was easily entertained and seldom bored, playing contentedly by myself for hours. But, periodically, the stultifying inertia of the house overcame my good humour and I sulked or went about, deliberately making noise in order to evoke sympathy for my unjust and protracted imprisonment. I sat in the shadows of the curtains of her room, kicking the furniture, too bored to even look out the window or play with the radio, chanting a cry of complaint, 'I have nothing in my hand', as though I expected someone to reach out and present me with an ice cream cone or some other token to distract my attention. There was a stirring from her bed and a summons.

'Come here, boy. What are you doing?'

'I have nothing in my hand!'

'Oh come here and we will see about that.'

Slowly I shuffled across the carpet and stood by her bed. Her face loomed out of the whiteness of the pillows.

'What have you got in your pockets, boy? Put everything out on the bed.'

Laboriously, I poked in the pockets of my short trousers, hoping that they contained no contraband. It was never clear to me at what the adult world might look askance. The most innocuous possession could be regarded with suspicion. First came an untidy length of string, then a metal washer, followed by some crumpled paper, the stub of a pencil and half a biscuit. An assortment of glass marbles was followed by the buckle of an abandoned dog-collar, originally belonging to Blitz, and various hardly identifiable bits of rubbish. She scrutinized the contents of my pockets as I laid them out on the counterpane of the bed. As though fascinated by my treasures, she said, 'All those things! How very interesting.' I stared glumly at the collection and repeated my mantra: 'I have nothing in my hand.' Now engaged, she proceeded to create out of the detritus of my pockets a suitable entertainment.

A skeletal hand emerged from under the bedclothes and picked up each item, rearranging them on the bed. Then she pronounced her verdict on my possessions.

'We will need something round [the washer], something thin and windey [the string]', and so she proceeded to identify each by its shape, even the half-eaten biscuit, 'That will be difficult. Something brown.'

I thought she had fallen asleep as she closed her eyes for a while, but she had been thinking and she opened them again, evidently quite awake. She scribbled something on the piece of paper with the stub of my pencil and sent me to the kitchen to it give to Mrs Luby, bidding me return promptly to the bedroom. For an hour she occupied me, sending me around the house to locate objects inspired by the contents of my pockets. From the Japanese cabinet in the cuckoo clock room, she directed me to bring something from one of its little alcoves decorated with ivory birds: a dark vase on which pranced a delightfully iridescent green dragon which circled around its girth. This she placed with the string, and their twisting movements and shape were similar. From Annie's room she requested a little blue glass bowl, into which the coloured marbles were placed. And so she worked her way through my things, identifying some quality in the mundane items which might be heightened by its relationship to something finer, involving me by making an adventure of the searches she directed. Then Mrs Luby arrived back from a shopping errand and sent Mary Mary upstairs with a plate of doughnuts. In the centre of the plate Grandmother placed the little brass washer, its shape perfectly replicating the sugar-dusted buns.

'Go on, boy, eat up. They are all for you.' My eyes bulged at the sight of such plenty. Eventually satiated, I brought the plate to the kitchen where Mary Mary revived from a mid-afternoon torpor and polished off the remainder.

Grandmother's historical reminiscences generally introduced me to her own youth and early motherhood, but gave little inkling of a topic I would have found much more interesting: my own mother's childhood. On the rare occasions when Grandmother responded to my presence, I stepped back a generation and became one of her children, my mother or her siblings. This was far more fascinating than the Great War, the focus of her general attention. As a proxy for her child (my mother), I could imagine myself to be somebody else whom I intimately knew, and I could enter a more gentle world where time moved more slowly. On these rare occasions, I felt that I was bringing her back to when she had small children of her own, and experienced how she related imaginatively to them.

On other days when the light from outside had invigorated her, or she was feeling more energetic, Grandmother sang songs of love, sadness and forgetfulness. These songs I had never heard elsewhere, but I recognized from the manner of her introduction that they belonged to a distant era. In Windermere we had a cabinet gramophone, successor of the earlier variety which had an external horn immortalized in the emblem of His Master's Voice (the firm which became HMV) of horned gramophone and attentively listening dog. Richard Tauber or some tenor of the early years of recording regularly performed on our gramophone, and his crinkly speaking voice, heavily Teutonic in its accent, began the recital with the words 'An I vill now zing vor you…' An zo he did.

Grandmother used the identical phrase, whether adopted from recorded music or because it was the form used in music halls of the Edwardian era.

'Boy, I will now sing for you "Beautiful Dreamer" by Stephen Foster.'

Her voice had little volume but was sweet and clear, usually ending on a high and unstable octogenarian quaver. She knew all the words and would sing as though giving a drawing-room recital. I felt that she was singing just for me, and although I feared my grandmother more than loved her, when she was singing I felt closer to her than in any other circumstance. Sometimes she would stop mid-verse to comment on a particular phrase, as though writing footnotes for a volume of songs:

> *Why should the beautiful ever fade,*
> *Why should the beautiful die?*

'Now that, naturally, is a question of considerable philosophic interest, but we must leave it for another day.'

Foster and Thomas Moore and similar sentimental drawing-room ballads formed the core of Grandmother's repertoire. Occasionally she sang to herself, alone in her bedroom, and her voice would waft thinly down to the distant kitchen as snatches of lilting words, always melancholy—usually the anguish of parted lovers. Then her attention had gone back to her first lover, who had died, and she was lamenting him. I never had the courage to ask about this person and neither the Rosenheim staff nor my parents ever mentioned a name, but I was sure that he had been both good and beautiful.

The poetry of empire dominated her literary terms of reference, and with the occasional Irish exception, might have been more representative of taste in Finchley or Grantchester than in Cork. However, substitute Queenstown for Cork and the lines which attracted her are perfectly consistent, the maritime and the heroic being her birthright. 'Drake's Drum' she could recite with surprising vigour and I loved her rendering of Sir Henry Newbolt's poem. I found it thrilling:

> *Drake he's in his hammock an' a thousand miles away,*
> *(Capten, art tha sleepin' there below?)*
> *Slung a'tween the round shot in Nombre Dios Bay,*
> *An' dreamin' arl the time O' Plymoth Hoe.*

My confused sense of national identity as a child (I did not consider myself confused at all, although my parents were convinced of the fact) clearly derived from having infused such attractive English heroics. Grandmother thought her heritage encompassed the best of the English-speaking world, and this I absorbed and accepted as my own. Were we not living in Windermere, made famous by Wordsworth? Grandmother's taste included much of the canon of nineteenth-century verse, and she could without effort reel off great quantities of poetry or doggerel, learned by rote during her youth. Her choices were always redolent of romance and tragedy. Wordsworth's 'Lucy Gray' provided her with a perfect image of courage, duty, and loss, but for me it was more personal, as I saw myself in the figure of Lucy Gray, remote and solitary.

> *Oft I had heard of Lucy Gray:*
> *And, when I crossed the wild,*
> *I chanced to see at break of day*
> *The solitary child.*
>
> *No mate, no comrade Lucy knew;*
> *She dwelt on a wide moor,*
> *—The sweetest thing that ever grew*
> *Beside a human door!*

On days when I was feeling neglected, I felt that the poem had been written just for me, in exile in Rosenheim, and wondered how Mr Wordsworth knew. Poor Lucy, sent to town by her father to accompany her mother home through the snow, gets lost, falls from a footbridge and is drowned.

> *'Tonight will be a stormy night –*
> *You to the town must go;*
> *And take a lantern, Child, to light*
> *Your mother through the snow.'*

CHAPTER 13

Among the black and white films made during the nineteen fifties, many are set during World War II. Of these a considerable number are accounts, true or fictional, of Allied prisoners-of-war, their defiance of Nazi captivity, and heroic or comic attempts to escape. On seeing one of these films, *Stalag 17*, during the nineteen sixties, a specific incident in the film attracted my attention and served to render harmless a gratingly unpleasant memory of my childhood.

The scene in the film takes place in a barrack building in which a squadron of American POWs have been assembled for haranguing by a senior German officer. The uniformed POWs are lined up in military rows, their backs turned to the camera as the stereotypical jackbooted and glowering German officer strides in. An NCO barks out an order, bidding them to stand to attention and turn around. This they do in clockwork unison, each with arm upraised in Nazi *Sieg Heil* salute, and with a black Hitler moustache painted on every face, then breaking into an outburst of laughter at the officer's outraged discomfort at this insult to his great leader. Whatever was the narrative point of the scene in the film, the object was to undermine German authority by ridicule.

I was reminded of a similar scenario, enacted in reverse order in Windermere, of an assemblage of uniformed officers sitting or standing in our drawing room and me outside in the hall, being prepared and prompted by my mother and Annie. My role was to impersonate the Führer. I was fat and round-headed, with very black straight hair (the last-mentioned at least was a tangible resemblance to the crazed Adolf's appearance) and my hair fell in a fringe to one side, as the Führer's did, a second point of parallel. With such natural assets, I was made up by the maid, who applied with burnt cork a dense and dark Hitler-like moustache to my upper lip, an operation I hated, although it did not hurt in any way. I merely disliked the sensation of the cork on my skin, and the smell of burning under my nose. The effect was undoubtedly ridiculous – Chaplin's *Great Dictator* in rotund miniature. Like a shy child in a Nativity play, with a gentle shove I was reluctantly propelled into the drawing room where the audience of my parents' friends dissolved with laughter, and I was awarded with loud clapping and repeated mirth. I rushed around the room to the further amusement of the adults, my very plump right arm raised in the air, and shrieking *Sieg Heil! Sieg Heil! Sieg Heil!* at the top of my very shrill voice, as though the Führer was being impersonated by a demented budgerigar. In the bunker below the Berlin Chancellery or at his retreat at Berchtesgaden, Mr Hitler (as he was respectfully referred to in the newspapers and radio broadcasts of the day) may have experienced a moment of unease—a goose walking over his grave—that such an absurd satire of his pompous and self-regarding person was being performed elsewhere in Europe by a small child. Dressed in my father's military peaked cap, his Sam Browne belt on my portly figure, I capered around the room, aping the German leader, yet unaware of the meaning of the gesture. Sometimes one of the officers would respond with '*Seig Heil, mein Führer*', replicating the leader's own strange ear-scratching salute in response, evoking further laughter from the audience. Whenever there was a large gathering of the captains and their queens, I was bribed with promises of treats to perform this charade until I became too embarrassed to do so any more, and with the ending of the war, the joke had palled and the humour had evaporated from any mention of Hitler. He just was not funny any more; he had become unspeakable, and I was released from my theatrical career.

The memory of this incident caused me acute embarrassment as a teenager, in what I interpreted as my parents' gross insensitivity and exploitation of my innocence for the amusement of their friends, until I saw the scenario replicated on film, set in the identical timeframe. Then I understood the psychological significance of the gesture of the POWS. Similarly, at a time when it seemed that the German forces were invincible and might win the war, to my parents and their group of army friends the ever-increasing threat was neutralized by turning Hitler, through the catalyst of my comic impersonation, into a figure of absurdity.

A more recent and further resonance was caused by seeing photographs of William Joyce, Lord Haw-Haw, in a British Union of Fascists uniform, his fringe slicked down as mine was, his look-alike Hitler moustache resembling mine as though it had been imposed on his face by his mother with the end of a burnt cork, his twisted smile idiotic and childish. That Lord Haw-Haw's image was known from the newspapers and cinema newsreels of the day, and that my comic resemblance to him in Hitler mode could only have added to the group's amusement at my impersonation, was catharsis certainly, but at the expense of my childish pride. I did not like impersonating Mr Hitler, whoever he was.

War preoccupied the adult world that surrounded me; its details frequently as illicit as sex or scandal. Naturally I was interested in anything that adults considered to be 'unsuitable'—if unsuitable for the ears of a small boy, it must be very interesting. The more the silences, the more I listened. I observed that life is lived on multiple planes of both meaning and ambiguity, that parents do not say everything to each other, that the maids who intimately shared the family life were 'with' but not 'part of' the family, that the neighbours' children with whom we played as close and inseparable friends were also potential spies, that all fact was circumscribed by interpretation: 'nuanced', an overloaded and overworked present-day phrase, is apt in the circumstances. Being a child in the nineteen forties was both idyllic and hazardous. According to the parental wisdom of the time, it was assumed that children lived in some prelapsarian world, understood little and should be preserved from worry and conflict. This utopian view was simultaneously contradicted by the fact that any observant child who saw too much would not have been thanked for advertising the fact. Lacking in tact or cunning, I frequently found myself on the wrong side of the divide.

The Hobbema 'Avenue' painting must have awakened in my dormant subconsciousness some sense of the duality of being simultaneously both present and absent. In Windermere there were numerous military photographs on display, including large group photos of Defence Forces staff officers. Many of those seated in the serried rows, as serious-minded and responsible men of action, came to our house as the laughing Falstaffian figures. The gulf between the image and the physical presence was too jolting to be ignored. Which represented the real person? I felt that I had isolated an essence of people's lives, something that was unclear in the daily imperceptible merging of one event into the next; you had your tea, you played in the garden, you went to bed. But in the photographs it had been captured that these laughing, hearty individuals had another self altogether, which existed in some other moment, quite distinct from the present one. In the photo there was no smell of polished leather, no clip-clop of hard footwear on the tiled floors, no acrid hint of Brasso.

Fuel was scarce during the war because no coal could be imported and Irish coal was of inferior quality and unsuitable for domestic use. But the army looked after its own. During a number of successive summers in the latter years of the war, a formidable military force, assembled to defend the island against invaders, was launched instead against the bogs of Ireland. The campaign was to keep the home fires burning. Having actually nothing to do but watch the coastline, follow up rumours of German spies being dropped by parachute or landed by U-boat (both were actually attempted and some spies did succeed in landing), the army was available for other duties. A German accent and a Bavarian greatcoat while ordering a pint in a wartime country town were hardly a guarantee of anonymity.

The prospect of some weeks on the bog harvesting turf seemed like an attractive option, as opposed to waiting for a German landing, which at that point, late in the war, the army knew was increasingly improbable. For weeks on end my father was away, supervising the cutting of turf by the privates, who laboured, as doubtless they had done on the farm at home and on their family's turf bogs before the war, with cups of strong tea as their reward. The result of the endeavour was a turf allocation to each family, the officers naturally getting a larger share-out than the 'other ranks', senior officers coming well out of the initiative. Beside our house, a turf-rick grew as the loads of fuel were delivered, until the entire area between the house and the boundary wall was occupied by the mound, as large as a thatched cottage, covered in tarpaulin and only very gradually diminished. This was to last us through the remainder of the war and for a year or two afterwards. My father was disappointed when the great turf-foraging expedition was over; the camaraderie and life under canvas which it necessitated was a welcome alternative to sitting at a desk, allocating fuel rations for military vehicles, or to hunt agents in *lederhosen*, attempting to buy a pint of *Munchnerbräu* in a backstreet bar in Mallow. This turf bonanza obviated the need for any further orders of fuel from Block and his master, much to my mother's relief, as my brother's implacable dislike for the boy had not mellowed.

Radical in some respects, my father was exceptionally conventional in others, in particular his expectation that Windermere was my mother's domain. When he came home, he assumed that she and we children would be there, and that, whatever about God being in his heaven, a mystical region in which my father displayed no interest, all would be right with the world. Their mutual relationship was one of affection and respect. They were not particularly burdened by economic woes or serious personal illness, therefore he expected that their neat little world would function as he wished it to, with clockwork regularity. A lifetime of army discipline and an unarguable routine had evidently convinced him that if the world conducted its affairs by an agreed timetable, then it would be a better place. The dramas and demands of Rosenheim were a constant intrusion into these programmatic aspirations and, if he had been away on manoeuvres, or some extended military business, it infuriated him to arrive home and find the house deserted but for the maid in charge of the children, his wife being away in Rosenheim. Although this den of confusion was a mere few streets away, he resented its constant intrusion on carefully structured domestic order.

At some particularly fraught moment in the affairs of Grandmother's ménage, my father contended that our family did not actually live in Windermere at all, but in a house halfway between it and Rosenheim. My mother, in an unwisely witty response, declared the residence of turmoil to be *Rosen-mere*. This drab residence, identified by its occupying the mid-point of the journey between the two houses, entered the family mythology as our actual house and when ironically referred to as where we had been was guaranteed to cause my father further annoyance: this was a joke he was not prepared to countenance. When, following some arduous journey in the cab of a military lorry from Monaghan or Meath, he arrived to find his house deserted and he set out for Grandmother's, it was with an ill grace and a worsening temper. For the mildest of men, he suffered from occasional rages, rarely to be encountered, but deafening in their volume.

Although he disliked going to Rosenheim if he had just ended a lengthy journey, my father had an admirable calming affect on the old woman. She regarded him as the image of masculine perfection, capable of solving all difficulties. This may well have been true, since he was immensely practical and the mundane utilitarian problems that beset Grandmother's domain (frequently of the minor plumbing or electrical genre) could generally be solved just by somebody making a decision, a process for which my mother had a practised aversion, equal to my father's disdain for a home untenanted by his wife. Having resolved the current difficulty, they returned home, he rebuking her for not maintaining a more satisfactory control of the Rosenheim staff. Mrs Luby's tenure was ritually threatened, but my mother, when faced with the task of replacing the housekeeper, just closed her mind to the matter—and opened her latest novel. If she thought about it at all, she would become upset, so the problem remained unresolved—until the next time.

With my father back from 'somewhere in Ireland', the location not revealed for reasons of wartime security, life continued its even tenor as they resumed their places at either side of the fire, read their books, exchanged news, or, as it might have been defined elsewhere, 'gossiped'. Still deemed not to have sufficiently recovered to attend school, I was daily shuttled between the houses. From my brother's school, tales of classroom life were always an insight into an unseen world that I had no inclination to explore. My (utterly unsuccessful) position as monitor of life in Rosenheim was still held in some slight esteem. For me, the entertainment value of my days at Grandmother's provided a context far more interesting than anything related from my brother's schooldays. I was content to remain there, with occasional lapses into petulance when I remembered poor Lucy Gray—'The solitary child'.

CHAPTER 14

I f Rosenheim exuded the decorative excesses of the *fin-de-siècle* mind, Windermere was minimalist in its aesthetic. The wall colours were light, the carpets monochrome, the ornaments predominantly Art Deco or Japonaiserie, not a William Morris swish or Celtic Revival sworl to be seen anywhere: the windows let in light! It was as though, to my child's sensibility, the houses were colour-coded as different, the dark tones and textures of Rosenheim contrasted with the openness and clarity of Windermere. But the concerns of war pervaded both houses; the trenches of the Great War evoked vivid emotions at Rosenheim, the current engagement of World War II preoccupied Windermere. However, since nobody had bothered to point out to me that these were separate conflicts, divided by a generation, I was under the impression that they were the same event which had been going on for a very long time, just named differently in the separate houses, in the same way as the vocabularies of their garrisons differed. Windermere favoured hot water bottle, radio, cinema and toilet, while Rosenheim had hot jar, wireless, picture house, lavatory, although my father frequently upset these precise linguistic demarcations by relapsing into the jargon of the other house and using 'wireless' instead of the more modern 'radio'. Even one's own name could change in the different jurisdictions: in Windermere, instead of our proper names, my brother and I were known merely by our initials as F., and B., whereas in Rosenheim I was both nameless and initial-less, being merely 'boy'.

I was acutely sensitive to difference, and the elusiveness of defining boundaries concerned me. Why things were different from each other was a continual question to be pondered. I was certain that if I could solve the enigma of difference, then I would be in possession of some essential truth: the difference between my father and my mother, between my brother and me, between the two houses. The father/mother issue I understood to be complex and involved ineluctable elements beyond my comprehension, but the two houses should, I concluded, be easier to unravel. Windermere, unquestionably a 'W' house, clearly pronounced itself as a building of pebbledash. I heard this term from my father and savoured it, rolling the phrase around in my mind, placing it in the air and mouthing it until I felt that it was the most precise description in the world, the epitome of exactness. 'The Greeks had a word for it' was one of my mother's favourite sayings, implying that precision of language and using the correct word were important aspirations because words defined thoughts. You could not express thoughts or feelings, she maintained, if you lacked the necessary vocabulary. I could see that the Greeks would be very pleased with 'pebbledash' as a richly descriptive phrase. The entire exterior of the house was covered in small varicoloured pebbles, set into a terracotta-coloured hard rendering. This was pebbledash and you could run your fingertips over the sea-worn smoothness of the pebbles and look closely at the 'dash' as I supposed the reddish cement to be called, and see that this was something perfect and pleasing. And then there was the bay window into the front garden, and the glasshouse which projected into the back and which had many sides and sharp angles. I liked these too, since they seemed to be so Windermerish and beyond being improved upon. I had found a nail in the garage and by diligently searching on the external wall at the side of the house, where I could not be observed, had located a loose pebble. With my nail, I prised it out of its little cushioning recession and carried it off in my fist, deeply buried in my trouser pocket. This pebble I took with me to Rosenheim as a memento of the other house, savouring its absolute smoothness and perfection until my father, observing that I had my hand permanently plunged in one pocket, enquired what I had in it, assuming that some contraband was being concealed, a stray penny found around the house. Forced to reveal my treasure, it lost some of its allure.

That I was so concerned with shape, form, texture and colour may appear unlikely, yet even the youngest of children's toys are designed to express precisely these formal qualities which would be meaningless unless it is assumed that the child is actually responding to just these aspects of the objects. I had evidently taken the primary stages of tactile learning a step further, in intellectually analysing the meaning and purpose of such qualities. I believed that the pebbles and their enveloping matrix held the secret of the house and our residence in it. One only had to look at Rosenheim, an 'R' house, to see how true this was. Every feature of both houses presented me with enigmas to be solved. Rosenheim was a grey house, as smooth as a paving stone, no pebbledash to be found there, no rosy colouring or shiny marbles to run your hand over. Rosenheim may have had a grey and unprepossessing cement rendered exterior, but it also had a lot of decorative timberwork, and stained glass in the hall door, in the dividing doors between the downstairs reception rooms, and along the top of the sitting-room windows. These features, particularly the stained glass, were for Rosenheim the elements that established its uniqueness. Once I was within Rosenheim's dark hallway, and the hall door closed behind my escort, I ran my hands over the cold coloured glass and tried to see into the depth of its shades. This was intriguing because the closer you put your eye to the glass, the more the colouring swam and the tints merged. There was a deep ruby red surrounded by some yellows, rich browns and greens, and every time I examined them I felt that the colours had changed, from the most pale translucencies of the rainbow to dense pools, as dark as ink, which indeed they may have done on account of the light conditions outside. Since this optical explanation never occurred to me, I was happy to re-encounter the glass each day and to see what the colours were doing, crediting meaning to their changes of tone and temperament.

But the profoundest difference in the two houses was not to be identified in colour or texture, nor in their inhabitants, but in the powerful sensation of the smells. Windermere was a monument to fresh air and cleanliness; it glowed and sparkled with the evidence of domestic involvement worthy of any German *überfrau*. Annie cleaned and polished, dusted and scrubbed all day long, other than when she was looking after my brother and me. My mother supervised, gardened or engaged in dressmaking on her sewing machine. The cleaning was like the painting of the Forth Bridge: once it had reached the last cupboard interior, it began again with the windows.

If Mrs Luby had been given a job description, it would have euphemistically mentioned some 'light housework' without itemizing the tasks, although she rarely did anything (even theft) which could not be achieved while sitting at the kitchen table. The maids, however, were expected to accomplish all work: to clean, and dust, and scrub, to fetch and carry, to run errands and go to the shops. This range of activities paid little attention to actually cleaning and, beyond superficial washing the hall floor as a public space, cleaning mostly amounted to the swish of a duster and the sweeping of rubbish under the corner of a carpet, a subterfuge at which all the Rosenheim maids were adept. It would never have occurred to me to spend time looking under carpets, but on some occasion I overheard my mother lamenting this trait, while stating that most of Grandmother's maids were lazy and incorrigible. I decided to put this new-found observation to the test and, on gingerly lifting the corners of a few Rosenheim carpets, discovered handsome deposits under each. As time passed, the house interior became grimier and dirtier and more relegated to being the home of the city's allotment of dust and carpet mites. Periodically, my mother or the aunt demanded that Mrs Luby institute a thorough spring-clean of the house, but this hardly succeeded beyond the opening of long-sealed windows. Fresh air entered into spaces for years deprived of even a breath of wind. In consequence, the smell was an overbearing one of the thick loam of dust overlying everything, beyond the concern of the passing maids, and years before the general appearance of vacuum cleaners.

During the summer months, both houses displayed fabric door-awnings, fashionable from the nineteenth century as sun-protection against blistering for the pre-industrial paint surface of the front doors. Hung over the door in vertically striped coloured patterns, they contributed to a joyous sense of summer having arrived, when they began to make their appearance on the streets. In Windermere our screen was brightly coloured in green, brown and ochre and had carefully tailored apertures for bell, letterbox and door knocker. These opening were trimmed by baize in some complementary colour, which framed the little openings to suggest a human face, the knocker representing the nose, the letterbox, the mouth. I looked forward to the arrival of these awnings on our street as a herald of long hot days. As in Windermere, at Rosenheim the door-screen was ritually brought out for the summer, but it was as faded as Grandmother's raven locks, having no more than the ghost of its stripes, in colours now hard to define. What might once have been blue and red now were more like tones of grey, much washed and faded by the passage of time. It had the same little openings, but also two extra ones as eyes in the face in order to let some residual light into the dark hall, revealing small sections of the stained glass. Inside the hall, this feature sent two narrow beams of light into its arboreal gloom, lighting up flashes of maroon on the dividing curtain, or highlighting a row of bobbles.

CHAPTER 15

My pleasure at receiving a child's illustrated encyclopaedia for Christmas was somewhat dimmed by an awareness that some pages appeared to have been torn from the book. Was the present not new? Its glossy and colourfully illustrated cover and crisp and pristine new-smelling pages, pungent with the scent of printer's ink, certainly suggested newness, yet the frayed ends of a few leaves were unmistakably clear evidence of something missing. I peered at the jagged ends and brooded about what to do. I had become enamoured of the idea of encyclopaedias on discovering at Rosenheim the long-forgotten *Children's Encyclopaedia* that belonged to my uncle when he was a boy. My interest in that book gave my mother the idea that a modern version would constitute a welcome Christmas present.

In the B section, a number of pages were undoubtedly absent and although the stubs of the pages were quite close to the binding, as though an attempt had been made to remove them without their loss being obvious, they were nonetheless visible. What clinched the matter for me—although it was some time before I became so forensic in my examination—was that the otherwise consecutive numbers of the pages leaped from 0 to 5 without explanation. This was suspicious. The present was not from Santa Claus, who still put in a token appearance in our house, although the reality of his person was not seriously entertained, or from my mother's sister, the aunt. She certainly was eccentric enough to purchase a damaged book, or to wilfully vandalize one, but the encyclopaedia was a present from my parents and, consequently, a source of my confusion. Could my scrupulous mother or father, book-respecting and careful of possessions, have purchased the book without noticing the missing pages? This proposition seemed unsustainable since books in our house were regarded with the honour due to cherished possessions; they were to be cared for and not used as playthings, or as aids to other games. They were our household gods. Books, so very convenient in shape and so solid, and ideal for building forts, towers, bridges and any number of possibilities, were banned from such abuses. All that they could be used for was reading or looking at the pictures, with the pardonable exception of pressing flowers or leaves, for which they were so admirably designed. Rather than to be later accused of damaging my new and expensive present, I wondered if I should point out the fault and seek an explanation.

Before the dog-leg of our street and Windermere, the road was bounded on one side by high walls behind which were the long gardens of substantial houses, while on the other side were the glasshouses of a market garden. The owners of the garden were friendly with my parents and occasionally brought, as gifts, baskets of whatever produce was then in abundance. For purposes unexplained, structures of bamboo in the shape of Native American wigwams or tepees were also used in some aspect of the enterprise, and I must have showed some interest in them when visiting.

One day some men arrived at our back gate from the market garden with a truck of bamboo and later in the afternoon, two extraordinary wigwams stood at the far end of the back garden, looking in miniature like one of those pictures of Native American encampments in the sepia pictures of the uncle's encyclopaedia. I had read all about the Choctaw, Chickasaw, Sioux, Cree, about the Plains Indians and the Six Nations, their culture and their history in the old encyclopaedia, and for a publication of the very early twentieth century, there was little that was patronizing in the text. The tribes were never presented as the victims of the ever-successful cowboys. Rather, they were depicted as protectors of the land, in tune with their natural world and altogether a noble people. This understanding was grafted on to the wigwams in which my brother and I took up residence for the summer and well into the autumn until it became too cold to remain outside any longer. The wigwams stood through a number of winters, but gradually their bamboo began to soften and sag in the wet weather. I used to look out through our glasshouse windows at the tepees in the rain and imagine myself living permanently in such a romantic structure. On this instance, although it was December, I retired to my wigwam with the new encyclopaedia under my arm and cogitated on the missing pages.

My mother was painfully honest and made a very poor hand of any kind of subterfuge. This meant that her only defence against a direct question which she was determined not to answer untruthfully, was to remain silent or to prevaricate: either response was equally revealing. When I remarked on the missing pages, she visibly coloured and said rather too brightly: 'Oh, those were pages that I thought would not interest you, and so I removed them.' I accepted this explanation until it later crossed my mind that I would like to know what those pages had been about, so I returned to the subject and asked. Abashed and cornered, she had no time to rehearse a little white lie.

'Babies', she replied.

'Babies?'

'I knew that you would have no interest at all in babies.'

'Were the pages about babies?'

'Yes, how babies are born.'

1. *Author (right).*

2. *Windermere recruits on parade.*

3. *The author's father, Captain Stephen Lalor, c.1935.*

4. *Captain Stephen Lalor, exercising, Cork Showgrounds, The Marina, Cork, c.1940.*

5. Fergus Lalor at Windermere, engaged in some complex research.
6. The author at the Windermere wicket gate, anxiously awaiting the milkman's horse.

7. & 8. Mistress and maid, the author's mother, Joan McNamara c.1939, and a Windermere maid,
identity unknown. Her horseshoe brooch may indicate her name.

9. Rosenheim; Grandmother, Hanna McNamara with her two eldest children, Jack, owner of the Arthur Mee Children's Encyclopaedia, *and Maureen, the aunt in embryo. A formally aproned maid looks from an upper window, c. 1910.*
10. Joan McNamara, the author's mother aged five, before her introduction to the burning of Cork.

11. Grandmother in striped blazer in the back garden of Rosenheim with her grandsons, F. and B., c.1944.
12. Grandmother at Windermere in full fox-fur travelling outfit.

13. *Hanna Griffin, the author's grandmother as a young woman with her cartwheel of copper-coloured hair.*
14. *Michael McNamara, the author's grandfather in debonair mode.*

15. Westview, Queenstown now Cobh, Co. Cork. Grandmother's house was in the middle of the terrace—halfway up, or down.

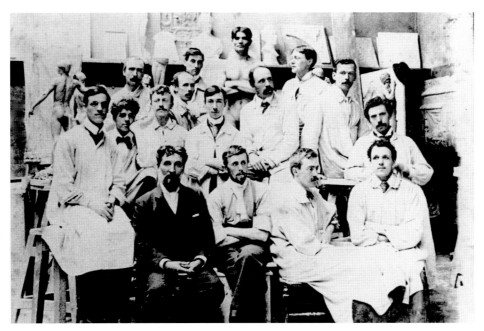

16 &17. 'Before and after' photos of students in the life modelling room at the Crawford School of Art, Cork, 1880s. (a) McNamara with moustache, to front right of model. (b) McNamara lower left having his moustache tweaked by a student. By the time the author attended the Crawford in the early nineteen sixties, some eighty years later, nude models had been banned from the College life room.

18. 'The Captains and the Kings', Commanding officer and staff of the 1st Division, Southern Command, June 1946. Commandant Stephen Lalor, front row right with riding crop. Six of those present including Stephen Lalor wear the medal ribbon awarded for active service during the War of Independence.

19. Commandant Stephen Lalor at Windermere, with characteristic ebony cigarette holder, c. 1950.

20 & 21. *Major General M. J. Costello (left) and staff officers studying troop movements on the Eastern Front, c. 1944. Commandant Stephen Lalor centre with cigarette.*

22. Joan McNamara in striped blazer, a style she appears to have adopted from her mother.

23. *The marriage at University College Cork's Honan Chapel of Captain Stephen Lalor and Joan McNamara, 1938. The pomp of the uniforms and the guard of honour of fellow officers are worthy of a Viennese operetta. Some of the Arts and Crafts Chapel's furnishings were by McNamara's students. Maureen McNamara, the aunt, is between the couple.*

24, 25, 26. M.J.McNamara modelling in the cast room of The Crawford School of Art, Cork, c.1919. (the building is now the Crawford Art Gallery). As tutor to Cork's most distinguished twentieth century sculptors, Joseph Higgins and Seamus Murphy, McNamara brought the French Beaux Arts sculptural tradition to Cork.

27. *M.J. McNamara at Tuirín Dubh in Gougane Barra, with fellow amateur revolutionaries, flanking a captive Celtic maiden. The play may be by McNamara's friend, Daniel Corkery.*

28. *Outing of a naturalist's club; McNamara is in the front row, extreme left. The group includes three clerics, a railway man and an undoubted toff in the back row.*

29, 30, 31, 32. M.J. McNamara, three studies from his period at the Royal College of Art, London, c.1896. Some of the drawings that survived the fire.

41 G. 3. R L.
Decorative Vorbilder Vol 5.

41 G

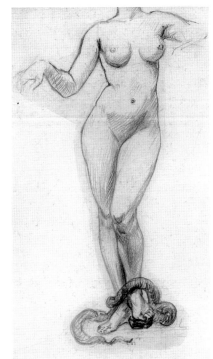

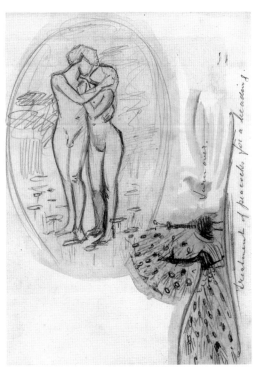

Armour from S.K.M.

¾ back view of shoulder piece

Short skirt of yellow velvet

This is considerably narrower on inside of arm.

33. M.J.McNamara, studies of medieval armour done at the South Kensington Museum, London, c.1898.

She nodded pleasantly as if to emphasize the utter triviality of such information, adding that she did not think that I would mind. She was perfectly right. I had no interest in or awareness of the matter of babies. I knew that I had once been a baby—all the family photographs testified to my pop-eyed existence as an infant—but up to that moment I had not been inclined to consider babies of any interest. In our street, proud elder sisters in their mothers' high-heeled shoes paraded on the pavement with new-borns in high prams, while in many front and back gardens, sleeping babies were an almost permanent fixture. They had sun shades, awnings, hoods to protect them from the weather, maids or family members constantly watching over them, shooing away inquisitive cats or swatting bumblebees and wasps. From my small-boy perspective, babies did nothing and were not notable for any perceptible attraction or contribution to the world.

But now that my mother had made up my mind for me that they were uninteresting, I became curious. That she had torn pages out of a book was unthinkable, and equally so that she might have destroyed these deleted pages. I decided to search for them. It was more that the topic of the babies was deemed to be uninteresting than the subject itself which aroused my attention. The issue became of interest purely because I had been told it was not so.

Amongst forbidden territories in the house was my parents' bedroom, so this looked like the place to begin my search and to satisfy my curiosity. While my mother had guests and Annie was in the kitchen, occupied in preparing for the visitors, I made my initial foray into their bedroom. The wardrobe was the first item of furniture inside the door, so I began with it, looking along the inside shoe shelves for what I now regarded as my pages. Failing to find anything, I next tried the dressing table and in one of the side drawers the bright illustrated pages, with their scarred edges, lay on top of cosmetic boxes from which, as soon as the drawer was opened, wafted that indescribably female scent of face-powder. The smell alerted me to my mother's presence downstairs and I went to the landing to listen to her talking in high-voiced animation to her friends, evidently narrating an amusing anecdote and unlikely to suddenly break off and come upstairs. At a superficial glance, the illustrations seemed confusing. Extracting the first page, I retired to my bedroom and studied it closely.

The encyclopaedia, superbly produced by some British publisher, with a hardback cover as shiny as a mirror, was illustrated by excellently graphic and colourful pictures. The book explained how the world worked, how sloths slept upside down, and diamonds were found underground. I was well versed in its revelations and entertained by this sustaining and attractive flood of information which each fresh examination provided. Sneaking back the first page, I took the second, and as I read and looked at the illustrations, my respect for the encyclopaedia faltered. The information on babies was so obviously incorrect (not that I had any alternative theory of my own on the subject) that I relegated it to the realm of the fairy stories I had now outgrown.

My mother had been right, I realized, to remove pages so manifestly inaccurate. I replaced the baby pages in her dressing table drawer and thought no more about the topic. Nonetheless, the failings of the baby-section in the encyclopaedia led me to a certain wariness with regard to what was presented as 'fact'. Clearly, on the evidence of including such a preposterous explanation, not every book of knowledge could be fully trusted, an intellectually challenging and valuable lesson for a youngster to absorb. As to the facts of birth and babies, I was unfazed by any conflicting personal version of the topic for, as my mother had so correctly surmised, to me the subject was of no interest. However, the fact that men and women were in some respect involved in the care of, and possibly the production of, babies seemed a given. Even if the encyclopaedia had got it all hopelessly wrong, I had subconsciously added the topic to my very considerable list of life's conundrums, the explanation for which I patiently awaited.

During the nineteen nineties, while editing *The Encyclopaedia of Ireland*, I came across Umberto's Eco's own thoughts on the problem of encyclopaedic veracity when he wrote: 'After all, the cultivated person's first duty is to be always prepared to rewrite the encyclopaedia.' Of course I already knew this from an early age. Perhaps Umberto's mother also had a penchant for editing her son's reading matter? 'Semiotics? *Umbertino, caro mio*, I knew that you would have no interest in semiotics.'

I did return obliquely to the question, some time after the babies incident, but from a very different angle. I spent a lot of time looking out of our gate, in what our resident and long-standing maid Alice called 'gawping' at passers-by. I assessed the neighbours and casual strangers by some personal system of ratings as to their interest: old people (unlike babies) were interesting because abnormal, children at the far extreme were like myself and of the most consuming interest since they represented a constant supply of potential playmates. More fascinating than these and captivating because they represented something which I could not adequately categorize, were young couples. Having but a hazy idea of the question of girls and boys and why they might be bracketed together, I was interested in any behaviour of either or both which came to my attention.

My favourite adult couple who regularly passed up the road were singular for such conservative wartime years; they represented either the last of the *fin-de-siècle* decadents, or the first of the beat generation. In either case, they were inexplicably and forlornly shipwrecked on this desert isle, home of the irredeemably drab and conventional. They were, for me, uncategorizeable other than being young: the man had shoulder-length bleached-blond hair, a dark, closely hugging suit, white socks and white leather shoes. His wife (for the concept of partner had not penetrated the south of Ireland in those distant times) was equally svelte in some ancestor of the mini-skirt, green stockings, and always wore impenetrably black sunglasses—in Cork in the late nineteen forties this alone was a statement of almost apocalyptic revolutionary intent, and a rallying call to the barricades. This wondrous couple preoccupied my thoughts, and I could spend days hoping that I might see them, peering out of the upstairs windows if I was not allowed out, wondering how I could discover who they were without asking any member of my family, who would immediately find my interest a cause for amusement or concern.

The subject, however, of my most passionate curiosity was a girl in red shoes. What else she wore was unimportant; the shoes were pillarbox red and lacquered so that they were visible through the legs of any crowd, glowing like beacons among such motley colours as were generally worn at the time. I wanted those shoes to the point that I wanted to be the girl with the red shoes. Week by week, waiting for the bus or going to or from town with my mother, the girl would appear with her otherwise uninteresting family, parading her shining footwear. She was about my own age, and the shoes were worn with long knee socks. Despite continuous efforts, I never succeeded in getting her to catch my eye. I did not want to alert my parents to my interest in the girl in the red shoes. My father would have been hugely entertained, my mother would have been perturbed—their conventionally different reactions to most issues.

I was a boy and clearly not going to be allowed to wear pillarbox red buckled shoes, and certainly not in combination with white, elasticated knee-socks. I pondered this issue and unfortunately, in the presence of both my parents, asked, 'Why could I not be a girl?' Predictably, my father dissolved into long and hearty guffaws, dropping his newspaper on the floor. Conversely, my mother was not only disturbed by the element of doubt in the question, but, having only male children, she was unsettled with regard to what would have been a happier outcome in the greater scheme of things: her desire to have daughters rather than sons. No satisfactory explanation or answer was offered to my question, other than their separate reactions, neither of which encouraged a return to the topic of sexual identity. For some considerable time afterwards, my mother continued to stare at me with evident distress. as though the question had revealed some unfathomable difficulty. However, I had avoided the main issue, which was to ask the question without revealing my obsessive interest in 'Red Shoes'.

If for some reason, 'Red Shoes' did not pass by Windermere during the week, then I had the enigmatic bohemian couple to hope for. Without either, days were dull and uninteresting. Then I overheard my parents discussing, in hushed tones, a local scandal, the fact that 'White Socks', whom I recognized in my father's disparaging comments about the length and colour of his hair, had been arrested. I couldn't understand why. Voices dropped further as I entered the room sideways like a crab, circling around the furniture, hoping to be unnoticed, trying to hear without attracting attention. The often stated 'little pitchers have big ears' was repeated and I was abruptly ejected. What this cryptic statement meant, other than that I was not welcome at that moment, was beyond my severely limited understanding. I had on numerous occasions scrutinized every picture in the house, of which there were many—square, oblong, round, oval—yet not a single one of them had ears, or any evidence of projections that might be considered as ears. Again, the adult world with its coded language and inscrutable logic baffled me.

'White Socks' and his companion were now gone. My father, referring to 'that pair of crooks', said 'in the clink, where he should be', adding to my linguistic troubles. I assumed that the clink, thinking of Grandmother's bells, was some kind of sound and I attempted to visualize 'White Socks' struggling in vain to get out of this uncomfortable position. However, I had got the general drift of his remarks.

My infatuation for 'Red Shoes' lasted about a year, although she never noticed me nor, so far as I was aware, did my parents become conscious of my obsession. My desire to be a girl and therefore be entitled to such exotic footwear did not outlast the day when 'Red Shoes' passed by the house but on this occasion in ordinary brown shoes. In an instant her fascination evaporated. Soon I could hardly remember what she looked like, unexceptionable enough in all probability. But my daily life was the poorer without 'Red Shoes' or 'White Socks' to give it titillation and some subversive and confused meaning.

There were moments when the evident perversity of boys merged with my mother's general apprehension about sexuality. Often, to her irritation, I followed her around the house, observing what she was doing. When I got bored with this, or was sent off to amuse myself elsewhere, I transferred my attentions to Annie. The maid's activities consisted of a day-long regime of domestic chores, cooking, cleaning and tidying. I admired her expertise on the stairs with a dustpan and brush and became disappointed when she refused my offers of help. I identified this aspect of the housekeeping routine as significant, requesting a dustpan and brush of my own as an auxiliary Christmas present—the toy steam train or fort of lead soldiers could be anticipated anyhow; this was to be an unexpected extra. My mother was confused by the implications of the request; she did not want a son who was a sissy. My father, consulted about this further crisis of identity, responded with vehemence. As a manly man, he issued an edict denouncing the request.

'If he wants a dustpan and brush for Christmas, he must be, as your termagant of a sister maintains, simple-minded.'

This engendered a struggle between my parents on the importance of not stifling initiative, which led to an impasse on the topic. Christmas came, Santa obliged, and a smart 'Little Bo-Peep Dustpan and Brush' set with a blue-handled sweeping brush also in the box, was found beneath the Christmas tree. The charm of this absurd gift wore off remarkably rapidly, and it was confined to some cupboard in my bedroom.

It was not long after my desire for sex change that I stumbled upon a topic even more controversial—the deity itself. My theological investigations within my family cannot be described as an unqualified success, and I might have chosen my territory of investigation more carefully. In Rosenheim the staff were generally approachable and happy to answer my questions. Religion, I had surmised, was an elusive and mysterious subject, and getting to the bottom of it was tricky. My new encyclopaedia was in this respect no help at all, since it failed to mention the subject in the manner in which I encountered it, as an extensive list of 'don'ts' and some highly improbable tales of divine carry-on. Certainly there was information in the encyclopedia on the physical manifestations of belief—Gothic cathedrals, the Kabba in Mecca, a Zen temple and St Paul's—but nothing as to what religion was all about, or why one should believe in its bizarre formulations. There was also my entire family's negative reaction to the often-mentioned 'peasant-beliefs'. Although I was not too clear on what these constituted, and had no idea as to who peasants might be, the definition seemed to hover around visibility—if you could see it, then somehow it was not acceptable. Cogitating on these great questions of life, like the missing pages of the encyclopaedia, I framed a question to launch a discussion. As in the incident of my desire to be a girl, my impulsive timing frequently was ill chosen. When my parents were sitting at leisure in the drawing room, in their respective armchairs on either side of the fire, overlooked by the comforting vista of *The Avenue, Middleharnis*, and with my brother and myself also occupied in reading, I decided to ask my question.

'Is there really a God, or is it something people pretend about?'

In a manner that might have been choreographed, my father lost the page in his book and, between fumbling to find it, smiled broadly and slapped the armrest of his chair in delighted mirth. He managed to knock his ashtray, attached to the chair arm by a weighted leather strap, on to the floor with his book. Overcome with amusement, he got up and left the room, ostensibly to summon Annie to clean up the mess from the ashtray. My mother stared after him for a moment, then at me, and put her face in her hands, sighing deeply. She gave a tearful sob and looked at me as though I had suddenly been diagnosed as mentally defective or terminally ill. My elder brother, clearly more astute in the ways of contemporary European thought, gave me a smart kick in the ankle, as though to say, 'Don't make such an utter fool of yourself', something I was unfortunately in the habit of doing on an almost daily basis.

Of course I never got an answer, my smarting ankle closest to an intelligible response, and eloquent in confirming my suspicion that indeed religion was a tricky topic that people were not disposed to discuss with the uninitiated; the world appeared to be divided into those who knew and those who did not. I could see no means of making the difficult transition from the position of the Don't knows. My father returned to the room, smiling to himself, and resumed his reading without further comment, twiddling the knobs of the radio as a diversion from discussion, while my mother sat brooding on the issue. She was not helped by her firm respect for the concept of freedom of conscience. To answer 'yes' to the first part of the question was not really possible since it implied an absence of doubt, whereas to answer 'no' was even more unthinkable because it suggested agnosticism. She began a meandering dissertation on personal conscience, which meant very little to me beyond suggesting that you could believe in anything you chose. So the topic lapsed and I was careful not to revert to it again. I had, however, got the point; from that moment on, religion and God would, for me, be other people's business and outside my horizon of interest. I had become a child atheist.

CHAPTER 16

On the days when Grandmother was feeling better, she liked to talk, always about the distant past, long before I was born and, in the manner of an orator, she monologued, while I listened as attentively as I could manage. Questions were neither expected nor welcome, although she could be illuminating if she considered that I was not being impertinent, inquisitive, or – the nadir of all behaviour—saucy. The danger of a question was that it could reveal some depths of ignorance so vast as to be unbridgeable, and the story would promptly cease, its conclusion unknown. She invariably began her reminiscences in mid-anecdote, without preamble, and frequently interjected different incidents into her narration without warning. It was easy for me to lose track of the where and when of it all. Periodically, a later version would contradict an earlier one.

'When she came home with a Shinner, I was aghast and furious. What would her father have said? I felt this betrayal deeply.' Grandmother paused and closed one eye while she considered her topic.

'Of course the girl was too imaginative and had no sense. What did she know of men? Nothing … and she was delicate. I forbade him to enter the house and told your mother never to mention him again. Anyhow, he was too old for her.'

Grandmother relapsed into silence and I contemplated the enigma of my mother with a black eye. I knew that a shiner was a vulgar word for a black eye, a term I was not allowed to use but which I had come across in my brother's comics. As usual, Grandmother's dialogue made little or no sense. I listened in the hope of enlightenment. Had my mother been in a fight? This seemed so entirely improbable that I consigned the topic to my store of unresolved mysteries: boys were frequently getting into fights on our street, and my brother often recounted similar schoolyard incidents. Girls I had never seen fighting and I recognized that my mother belonged in the girl department. I felt that this might not be a topic to be pursued at Windermere since there was implied criticism, which my mother would not welcome. Nonetheless, it provided food for speculation.

'Of course on this occasion I was wrong. He was a gentleman, even if a Shinner.'

While I was contemplating this enigma, the old woman's mind had slipped back a generation and, without warning, as I attempted to unravel what she had been talking about, she began a further reminiscence. My mother had now regressed in the story from being a woman of marriageable age to that of a child.

'I said to your grandfather not to do it, that I would be sick for a week (which I was—in fact, I think that I have never recovered from the shock, even now). I said that he would scar the child for life and possibly cause her to have hysterical fits. He took no notice and did it anyhow. Your grandfather had to carry an official pass from the RIC in order to go to the School of Art. If he was late or did not come back from his teaching, I was sure that he had been shot. Sometimes it was too dangerous and the RIC would warn him that there was shooting and he stayed in the School overnight. We had seen the glow of fires in the sky and heard gunshots from around the city. Neighbours and passers-by brought the news.'

'Your mother was only seven and I said to him that it was wrong to bring a girl, and a sensitive one at that, to see such things. He replied that it was his duty to let the child see, in order that she would remember what had been done. So they set out the day that martial law was lifted and before the trams had started to run again. They were gone for hours. I was terrified that one of the burning buildings had fallen on them. When they came back, your mother was as white as a sheet where she was not black with soot from the smoke and fires still burning: her pinafore was covered in grime—I never succeeded in getting all the soot out of it. Her hair smelled of smoke for a week afterwards and she would talk of nothing but what she had seen. I never forgave him for it, but he was a man, and so not susceptible to reason.'

This was my introduction to the burning of Cork by the Black and Tans in 1920. I went home to ask my mother if Grandmother's story was true, that the city had been set on fire and that her father had actually brought her as a child down into the city centre after the burning, just so she would see and remember it? She confirmed all the details, precisely as Grandmother had described them, except that her narration had omitted the important fact that they had met lots of people whom her father knew, including a number of friendly RIC officers who lived in their neighbourhood, that she had had delicious tea and cakes in a café in a street where business was undisturbed, and that she had greatly enjoyed the adventure.

'However', she added, 'Mother took it so badly that she was in bed for days, crying and lamenting, and that made me miserable. I said to Father that if the Tans burned the city again, I wouldn't go to see it. The fear of something happening to us had made Mother so upset.' The prospect of being brought to see an event as exciting as a city on fire appealed greatly to me and I felt that I too would like the opportunity.

'And would you bring me if Cork was burnt again?' I asked, anxious not to miss the excitement of a city in flames.

'Positively not, and if your grandmother mentions the topic again, please do not even suggest it. She will see the idea as a further example of bad upbringing.'

My mother added another detail to this particular incident, or rather to related days: that she had been sent for a message around the corner to a neighbour's house and had seen blood on the pavement. When she returned home and told her mother about the little red stars on the ground—splats of human blood—Grandmother took to her bed. Forgetting that a young man had been shot dead there the previous day, she had sent her six-year-old daughter on an errand, although she must pass by where the incident occurred.

Grandmother returned frequently to the topic, always with a slightly different slant or even with totally different details, but invariably concentrating on the great hurt that had been done to her by exposing her youngest child to such violent sights. But more frequently than the burning of Cork, she became exercised by the simultaneous losses of World War I or, as she referred to it, the Great War, the conclusion of which had immediately preceded the burning of Cork. I accepted that in Windermere, for reasons unknown, the war was merely 'the war', whereas in Rosenheim it was 'the Great War'. The population of Grandmother's road and neighbourhood had been severely hit during the Great War. Young men from many families, although not from her own, had been killed in the war and she continued to mourn this loss all her life. The dead and the war wounded were a constant refrain and, as I had seen, the shell-shocked had a very real presence in the neighbourhood. Because my own road had been built in the late nineteen thirties, the residents were younger, and the sight of war-damaged men unknown. Rosenheim stood in the heart of a professional middle-class district and it is likely that those from the area who had served in the British Army in World War I did so as much from young men's spirit of adventure or belief in the cause of 'the safety of small nations' as from loyalist sympathies. However it was economic necessity which drove many of the sons of the buildings into the trenches. The result was the same, irrespective of social strata: a black-bordered announcement in the *Cork Examiner*, and sometimes (if the victim was of officer rank) an image of the deceased, uniformed and looking jaunty with clipped moustache and swagger-stick in a studio photograph.

When I asked Grandmother questions, she became so infuriated, she frequently just lay back on her pillows and went to sleep, distressed by my apparent ignorance.

'Those parents of yours must teach you nothing. Your brother at least is paying attention at school and reads from the newspaper like a BBC announcer.'

I understood that it was much safer not to ask. Besides, if she became annoyed, one was in danger of never hearing the end of the story; then I would have to pursue the tale when I got home, with the likelihood of a less dramatic telling than Grandmother's version. Life seemed just so replete with fighting, soldiers and difficulties for there to be any possibility of unravelling the separate strands of who was whom, what happened when, or on which side we were actually supposed to be.

Another aspect of Grandmother's talk concentrated on more cultural perspectives, and explained the political sentiments of her late husband. Grandfather had been a dedicated cultural nationalist and Arts and Crafts Movement pioneer. In this complicated dispensation, the espousal of Celtic interlace as a decorative gospel for all occasions seemed to have supplanted the need for armed insurrection or heroism on the battlefields of Europe. I had not been impressed by the question of shell-shock and resolved that I at any rate would not be going to the trenches, unless of course it was something compulsory which just happened to one, like being sent for a haircut. At least in the Arts and Crafts belief system, the ideas of some Celtic nirvana intersected with the tangible, and the furnishings of Rosenheim made this strange philosophy visible. In every room were items of furniture, ceramics or wall hangings decorated in a Celtic Revival swirling interlace manner, tables and chairs, mirror and picture surrounds with biting serpents and complicated snake-like designs. This was the Gaelic equivalent of Secessionist Art Nouveau and a conscious political statement of Irishness between the eighteen eighties and the end of World War I. Grandmother's conversation certainly made these strange objects more understandable: they were a definite statement of who we were, not tainted by politics or religion. She began another of her monologues.

'Your grandfather insisted that we go every year to Ballingeary in west Cork and stay at the Irish-speaking household of the Ó Tuama's at Tuirín Dubh, where he could learn Irish. Of course he never bothered to learn a single word, nor, I think, did he have the slightest intention of even trying. It was merely an excuse for adventures, and provided an opportunity to be around the young men who held more radical views. I told him time and again that this would lead to trouble, but he was impervious to advice. I knew it would end badly.'

She relapsed into silence and when I looked at her closely, she was fast asleep. Her tales exhausted her, and she rarely managed to end a story in a single telling. However, on the following day she would resume, as though she had just mentally turned down the corner of her page (a book-reading habit very seriously frowned upon in Windermere). She then opened one eye and said 'Always respect your father' before dropping back to sleep.

It was to the same Tuirín Dubh that the son of an RIC constable, Johnny Whelan, a young revolutionary and language enthusiast, went to stay during the nineteen twenties. He returned at the end of the summer transmuted into the person who was to become the writer Seán Ó Faoláin, so I expect Grandmother did have a point; they were living in dangerous times and, for a cultural nationalist and pacifist, my grandfather was treading very close to the gunmen.

'I was right naturally. The last time I ever went there—it was in, I think, 1920 (afterwards I absolutely refused to go)—we were staying at Tuirín Dubh when it was raided by the Tans. Your grandfather's name was taken, and I was convinced that he would lose his post in the School of Art, but he thought that he could charm his way out of any difficulty by a twirl of his moustaches. Only when we got home did he tell me that there had been half-a-dozen rifles in the house at the time. But since the family had warning of the raid from a friendly member of the local RIC, they warmed them over the range and put them under the mattress of their dying mother. She was so obviously on the point of death that even the Tans did not disturb her. When he told me that, I went into a serious decline with the shock.'

My emerging picture of Grandmother's life in earlier times seemed to differ little from that of her habits as an elderly woman, with frequent lengthy recourses to her bed, and tears on many occasions.

'Wasn't I right, boy, to be fearful? Look what happened then? The following year, when I begged him not to go to Tuirín, he insisted in doing so and on taking the three children with him. I said that he was being foolish, which as a man of great dignity, he took a long time to forgive me for. Of course he was a fine man, honourable and caring, but reckless. They were driving along in the Model T Ford, and he was looking at the countryside as usual, admiring the sky and cloud formations, looking for castles and antiquities, not looking at the road. He was enjoying himself, and failed to notice that the local IRA boys had blown up one of the small bridges. So they drove off the edge of the bridge and landed in bushes in the river. The Ford was ruined but, apart from shock and bruises, they were unhurt. They carried on to Tuirín on some farmer's cart that they met a little farther along the way. They lay on the straw and laughed at their mishap. Your grandfather was regretful at the fate of his car—as a fine craftsman, he had great respect for anything well made—but he was careless on a practical level. Your mother and your aunt and uncle might all have been killed.'

What exactly *was* Grandfather doing in Ballingeary? Enjoying himself evidently. In a sequence of photographs taken there in the pre-War of Independence era, he was, it seems, involved in amateur dramatics and in visiting antiquities sites (typical pursuits for Arts and Crafts enthusiasts). The identity of a play recorded in one sequence of photographs has not been established—tiny box Brownie images with a white border, yet sharp enough to give good definition. He is seen with two fellow thespians, posing in costume on a country road, during a pause between rehearsals. The woman in the centre is wearing a Gaelic Revival dress with interlace embroidery and a cloak. This costume immediately suggests a Yeatsian drama of the Sidhe hosting in the air over some windy crag, but the men flanking her are armed with Boer War issue Lee Enfield rifles. However this play-acting scene must have taken place in an period devoid of revolutionary activity, because the armed actors are benign-looking and obviously dressed up. The other man merely wears a large flat black beret, riding britches and boots and is holding a pistol and rifle. Grandfather has adopted a rather more romantic, if no less militant, stance. In one hand he brandishes a pistol and over his shoulder carries a rifle, but it is his clothes that are so striking. He wears a woman's fur coat with the sleeves torn off. This is tightly belted, and on his head he has an Albanian peasant's cap with little pom-poms. The effect is of some follower of Byron, a Hellenic patriot and poet of the soil. Whether they have arrested or kidnapped the smiling Gaelic damsel, or are protecting her is unknown. Other photographs show him with various groups of people—on outings to historic sites, or beside bleak lakes. In one photograph, in which he is at his most Proustian, he is lounging in the front of a formal portrait group (a naturalists' field club outing perhaps) so possessed by ennui as to suggest that nothing could be more tedious than the proceedings. Clearly he *was* having a good time.

My grandmother knew, of course, that I would repeat all her stories when I returned home to Windermere, and part of her purpose was her projection of herself as a wronged woman, too highly strung for domestic dramas, and now, living in a house with an indolent housekeeper, a slovenly housemaid and a child, neglected in her declining days by her daughter. Back in Windermere, I quizzed my mother on the story about the wrecking of the car.

'Yes,' she said; 'it was just like that, except that your grandfather was very well aware we might all have been killed. He just never admitted the fact to Mother. We were lucky that the car landed in thick bushes, which cushioned its fall in the centre of the small river. It was in August or September, and the water came up only to the top of the wheels. For a while we just remained in the car—we hadn't fallen far—until Father decided that we would just wade to the bank with our bags and carry on. He was actually very shocked but tried not to show this.' She paused, then ruminatively continued: 'Your grandmother's stories are usually quite true; the difference is that she very easily becomes emotional, so events swiftly get out of proportion in her mind.' A 'drama queen' might be a reasonable modern interpretation.

Her monologues circled around the events and the losses of the Great War and 'those dear boys'—the sons and husbands of many of her friends who had been killed, and in their memory both she and Grandfather assiduously wore the poppy on 11 November, Poppy Day. The emblem was then widely sold in the streets of Cork, right throughout the period of the burning, the raids and the ambushes. Nothing was as likely to send her off into a vein of deep melancholy as remembrance of 'those dear boys', and sometimes I succeeded in heading her off by a well-placed question about something neutral, if I saw the populous trenches looming in her talk.

The sinking of the *Lusitania,* with great loss of life, was another of her favourite themes. This had happened in May 1915, off the County Cork coast, when a torpedo from a German U-boat sank a Cunard passenger liner, bound from New York to Liverpool. Grandmother's family was still living in Queenstown, and it was there that the survivors, as well as the bodies of the drowned, were brought. Her family was amongst the large numbers of townspeople involved in the rescue and the recovery of the bodies.

'My Uncle Dick was engaged in taking his boat out into the harbour and along the coast, searching for bodies. He rescued many, still alive, but mostly found the drowned floating amongst the wreckage. These he brought back to Queenstown, he and the other men, crewing his boat. They made dozens of journeys throughout the day and night until they were too exhausted to continue. Dick sat down on the floor of the bar in one of the waterfront pubs where the bodies were being laid out, since the town morgue was already full, and fell asleep. The bodies of the drowned were streaming water, and so was he, wet to the skin. When he awoke hours later, everybody thought he was one of the dead resurrecting and rushed in a panic from the building. Only when he walked out did they recognize him as Dick. The owner of that pub, another relation, lost his mind, ran about the streets saying that people were accusing him of having taken valuables from the dead. Many people in the town were deeply disturbed by the tragedy.'

That my memories might be less than reliable or indeed completely imaginary has of course frequently occurred to me. Over forty years after I listened patiently to Grandmother's ruminations on the Great War and its losses, this theme received confirmation (five and a half thousand men killed every day for four years) a statistic that would not have been available to her, but then she did not need the statistics, the central point of lives wantonly scattered like poppy petals was her enduring refrain.

One day while visiting my mother during the late nineteen eighties, she asked me to buy some new oilcloth for her kitchen table. I telephoned from Cork city centre to say that there was a choice between expensive and tasteful Tiffany designs, and the cheap and cheerful of bright flowers. She replied that it was only the kitchen table, and cheap and cheerful would be perfectly fine. Without further thought, I purchased some garishtly patterned oilcloth, delivered it to her in a package, and thought no more about it. A few days later I received an outraged phone call.

'How', she asked, 'could you be so insensitive as to give me that oilcloth?' I responded that she had specifically told me to buy the cheap and cheerful. The problem was otherwise.

'I couldn't possibly use it; the pattern reminds me of all those dear boys in the trenches.'

Slowly, the nature of my offence dawned on me. The floral pattern was of large poppies, gaily strewn on a trellis background, and the flower brought her immediately to the event it still represents on Poppy Day, even if this commemoration has been for many years suppressed in the Republic of Ireland. Her words exactly replicated those of Grandmother, carrying, a generation on from my mother's own childhood, the sense of loss that followed the carnage of the Great War, and which led to the proliferation of cenotaphs all over Britain. Although less common in the south of Ireland, the Great War cenotaph in Cork, with a low-relief effigy of a tin-hatted Tommy with bowed head, occupies a prominent position in the city centre. When my mother eventually left her house, the offending poppy oilcloth was found, still folded in its brown paper package in a kitchen cupboard.

Later, during the nineteen nineties, in researching aspects of Grandfather's career as a sculptor, I searched through the microfiche files of the *Cork Examiner* for the Great War years, post 1916. The respectful black-bordered obituary notices of local men killed in the trenches of France and Turkey are side by side with reports of republicans killed or arrested for insurgent activity. In the succeeding three-quarters of a century, these parallel events have been officially denied, with all the intolerance of the Soviet rewriting of history, in favour of an Ireland touched solely by the spilling of republican blood.

CHAPTER 17

Whenever it was reported to Grandmother from the kitchen that I had done less than justice to my dinner, cooked by Mrs Luby (complaining about how put upon she was with so much to attend to—worry about the old lady, the maid, and many more spurious responsibilities), Grandmother invoked the shade of the Armenians.

'Are you not ashamed of yourself, boy, leaving good food go to waste? Remember the starving Armenians.' Sometimes she varied her terms of reference and, in deference to the current conflict, mentioned 'the starving children in Europe', but I had less interest in them than in the Armenians, whose name attracted me.

After a decent interval I slipped away and asked in the kitchen about the Armenians and their troubles, but either Mrs Luby did not know the answer, or was not disposed to explain. I carried the question home to Windermere and requested my mother to tell me who the 'R-meenyans' were and what had happened to them. Extremes of behaviour or emotion caused her acute anxiety: she was happiest or most secure when engaged in some febrile atmosphere of witty exchange or serious conversation. Excesses of poverty or violence she could cope with in novels, but not in real life, where she protected herself, and was protected by my father, from distressing information. He habitually censored from her knowledge the more gruesome realities of World War II. The prospect of having to answer her younger son's questions, and the duty of contributing to the development of the child's enquiring mind, were balanced by the fact that the historic topic was not a pleasant one and such details as she recollected being discussed during her own childhood were horrifying. She approached the issue from a different tack, hoping to justify her response by her sincerity, without having to travel any farther east in the direction of Armenia than the centre of Cork. By substituting a local encounter with loss and deprivation for a foreign one, the Armenian holocaust would possibly be transformed into something unthreatening. In a meandering and half-reluctant manner, my mother related an incident that had occurred in the city during her early college days, which had left her with a searing recollection of abject poverty. Her mind always worked like this, making astonishing leaps of association, logical if carefully analyzed, but on the immediate occasion often difficult to follow.

A family friend or relative, who owned slum properties in Cork, was motoring on business through the city with his daughter and my mother in the back seat of his open-topped saloon car. This must have been in the late nineteen thirties when she was already at university and more exposed to the world than when she was younger and under the protective thumb of her parents. The car negotiated the mean streets and lanes on the flat of the city in an area known as the Marsh, until they were parked in a dark street of ravaged eighteenth-century tenement buildings, the narrow pavements and rutted roadway reeking of drains and uncollected refuse. The driver left the car parked in the middle of the street with the two young women chatting in the back while he entered one of the buildings. He told them to remain in the car until he returned. If another car (improbable in this quarter) or horse-drawn vehicle came down the street, it would just have to wait. Urchins and slum-dwellers stood or played in the doorways and either took no notice of the car and its occupants, or, in the case of the small boys, stared at the car admiringly and attempted to engage the young women in conversation. They sat there for some time, uncomfortable at being stared at by an entire community, even if there was no threat or evident hostility. These were precisely the type of street urchins they had always been told to avoid, and now they were forced to sit amongst them, attempting to avoid eye-contact.

While they waited, observing at least the outward displays of tenement life, a bedraggled and shawled woman carrying a heavy saucepan emerged from one of the open doorways and screamed up and down the street, summoning her children. They came running, a number of small undernourished-looking boys and girls, and stood expectantly waiting at their mother's heels. She sat down in her doorway and emptied the contents of the saucepan, a pile of boiled potatoes, on to the step. The children grabbed them and, peeling the skins, began to eat the hot, soft contents with their hands. Leaving them to their meal, the woman disappeared indoors with her saucepan, but not before screeching at the startled occupants of the car, 'Ye can park somewhere else if ye don't like to see them childers having their tay.'

My mother and her friend, upset at being shouted at by a ragged stranger, gazed with some astonishment at the scene: four or five small children eating potatoes off the step, without plate, knife or fork, relishing the hot and filling meal. Having consumed two or three potatoes each, the children sat in the doorway, digesting their meal and laughing at the embarrassed young ladies. The driver emerged from the building, his business completed (the collection of rent or the eviction of a tenant?) and resumed his place at the wheel, taking in at a glance the astonished faces of the girls in the back of the car and the row of dirty faces. With a nod towards the now smiling urchins, he uttered the single word 'Pigs' and drove off with a flourish, hustling some loiterers out of the gutter on to the pavement in fear of their lives. Back in Rosenheim, to Grandmother's visible distaste, my mother recounted the afternoon's sojourn in Cork's lower depths. Her mother responded with an Olympian disdain that sealed the encounter in amber, and closed off any possible discussion of the *alfresco* dining habits of the very poor.

'My dear, we shall not mention this again. We never discuss such things.'

Seeing that the story had ended and my question remained unanswered, I returned to the subject with razor-sharp attack.

'And were the children Armenians?' I asked. My mother gave me a suspicious glance and hastily left the room, her stratagem of engaging in metaphor as a means of avoiding the historic issue having failed to mollify her questioner. More troubling for her was having cast a shadow on the otherwise faultless wisdom of her beloved mother, by inadvertently suggesting that Grandmother might have been indifferent to the living conditions of the destitute, or too snobbish to care.

In my mother's emotional range, great human or natural catastrophes were too painful to be contemplated. By substituting local deprivation for genocide against the Armenians, she had hoped to insulate herself emotionally against the greater tragedy, yet had merely succeeded in confusing her child and disturbing herself. A swift immersion in the world of fiction was her invariable antidote to any intrusion of unacceptable truth, even when, as on this occasion, it was self-induced. And so the Armenians joined God and babies in my portmanteau of matters requiring further private investigation.

CHAPTER 18

My parents did not gossip, or at least they did not engage in what they regarded as gossip, a practice which they believed preoccupied the lower orders of society, and pretty much everybody else as well. Not engaging in gossip naturally preserved them against the even greater social evil of malicious gossip, of which they vehemently disapproved. How they actually ever gained any information about their neighbours, other than by osmosis, was through what they would have regarded as purely conversational means, and through the power of my mother's rich creative imagination. As chief source in our family's information on activity in the neighbourhood, she derived most of her knowledge from speculation rather than hearsay. The facts of the matter were infrequently ascertained and were regarded as being of marginal relevance.

If I went out walking with her, to town for shopping or to visit friends or relations, she would comment on the people we passed in the street; on the owners of the houses on the adjoining streets, on the passengers on the bus, on anybody who came to her attention, whether for their eccentricity of dress or the sheer banality of their appearance. Much of this observation would have done credit to Sherlock Holmes. She noted the condition of their shoes, and speculated on what a brown paper package, double-tied with green string, might contain; where a letter in an air-mail envelope, firmly held in some person's hand, might be destined.

'Brazil', she announced, 'to a cousin who runs a puma farm in the uplands. They export furs to Paris and Vienna, and have supplied most of the monarchs of Europe with coronation robes. Another cousin in Peru is an expert on exotic butterflies.'

Always I was enthralled, never quite sure whether she was fantasizing or had observed some small yet conclusive clue. A poor judge of character where her friends were concerned, my mother's command of circumstantial detail was impressive. If challenged, she frequently would respond with some well-observed and logical basis for her speculations. 'Did you not notice that her tippet was of puma? That is quite uncommon.'

The great merit of this type of information-gathering is that it need never be put to the test. That a particularly stout woman with a mend in the hem of her overcoat, and who habitually carried an umbrella, had been designated as suffering from claustrophobia, or that a young man who wore orange gloves was identified as a penniless Albanian prince, living incognito for fear of assassination, seemed credible enough and never required supporting evidence. The man, seen independently by me when on an errand, was casually referred to as 'the prince', and took on the exotic aura of an émigré aristocrat, while the stout woman became 'Mrs C.' and was noted familiarly when observed.

That my mother might have been accused of having an overly developed sense of fantasy would have been a fair criticism. She read voraciously, always fiction, and when not immersed in the latest novels, consumed the more cerebral end of detective fiction by the shelfload. All these manifestations of concern for her fellow mortals were fuelled by the nature of her reading. A survey of her bookshelves and library-borrowings might have revealed that émigré Albanian princes or stout claustrophobic women were commonly to be found amongst the guests at small hotels or isolated country houses to which a certain Belgian gentleman, M. Hercule Poirot, or a loquacious spinster, Miss Jane Marple, happened to call (but separately of course). For my mother, literature and life were inextricably entwined, and every chance encounter amongst those waiting to be served in the butcher's shop might prove to be the murderer in a criminal investigation not yet publicly announced. No one could have accused her of being a gossip, malicious or otherwise, but if the facts of her wild imaginings were publicly known, she might have been cautioned by the police for, at the very least, harbouring intentions to defame or slander strangers.

Opposite our most convenient bus stop was a terrace of rather nondescript late nineteenth-century houses. In the front garden of one of these stood a magnificent and mature monkey puzzle tree, much too large for the modest garden it occupied. A solitary elderly man lived in 'Monkey Puzzle House', and he often paraded up and down on the pavement in front of it, like a prisoner taking exercise in a detention yard. My mother provided him with a biography fitting the owner of so fine a specimen tree. The Monkey Puzzle Man (and here literature and reality merged) had been with Holmes at the Reichenbach Falls when the great sleuth, in the struggle with his adversary Professor Moriarty, had fallen to his death. The man, who had a limp, a dark complexion and thick black bushy hair, had been injured in the struggle. He was, we were reliably informed, Holmes's Greek manservant, Yannis, living out the remainder of his days, far from his native Delos (never mind any inconsistency of a time-lapse, or other irreconcilable details). It was curious, of course, that Conan Doyle had failed to mention Yannis, but, then, my mother had access to classified sources, and Holmes himself was notoriously evasive.

Aversion to gossip did not preclude my mother from being closeted in the kitchen with the maid while the latter related some lurid story picked up in one of the illicit small shops, conversations from which I had been summarily ejected. What distinguished my mother's definition of gossip was not the receiving of slanderous and scurrilous information from others, but the passing on of it to third parties: this she forbore to do, being satisfied in knowing that young Timmy Larkin from the end of the street had spent a month in jail for shoplifting, or that his father had lost his post in an insurance brokers, having embezzled a client's funds. These facts enabled my mother to view the said malcontents with supreme disdain when encountered on the street, conveying to the spurned ones precisely the impression which she wished to avoid, that she had been gossiping about them.

However, the human desire to divulge was often stronger than her principles, so she had to devise some means of accommodating her urges to her ethics. The Reillys are a case in point. They lived in an isolated house on the edge of the city and we visited them occasionally. The wife and my mother had been at college together, had married at a similar age, and had two children each. The husband had been a successful journalist and newspaper editor, with every appearance of being an upright citizen and pillar of the community, but had suffered a serious decline in his fortunes. He also had some odd habits. These included bouts of excessive and extended drinking, during which his journalism would collapse and have to be, with difficulty, resuscitated when he resumed normal life. During his drinking bouts, always conducted at home in a locked bedroom, he felt the encumbrance of clothes to be unsustainable, so he refused to wear any, irrespective of the time of year. In preparation for one of his marathon boozing sessions, he laid in cases of whiskey, enough to stock a substantial pub for some weeks. This diet nourished him until he was too ill to even drink. Then he emerged from his room, naked, and laid about the household with a knotted towel soaked in water. Wife and children fled, the police were summoned, the drunk was carted away and dried out. He eventually returned, abject, ashamed and seeking forgiveness, pledging abstinence and a determination to resume his lapsed profession.

We visited the Reilly household during one of the husband's periods of 'illness', in fact at an exceptionally inopportune moment when he was in a late-binge, hypersensitive state, and given to banging on the locked door of his room with an empty whiskey bottle if anything disturbed his meditations. With four children in the house, silence was impossible to sustain. It is very difficult for children, however often they have been enjoined not to ask questions, not to ask them wordlessly when the occasion arises. The wet and damaged state of the house, evidence of the husband's furious forays, the general lacklustre demeanour of our hosts, the thunderous noise and shouting from down the corridor, to which no allusion was made, did not make for a comfortable visit.

Sent to play outside for fear that we might further anger the enraged Polyphemus in his cave, our games fatefully brought us to the side of the house where his bedroom window overlooked the garden and where, amongst the rosebushes where he had flung them, lay an impressive pile of empty whiskey bottles. The Reilly children habitually acted as though nothing untoward was taking place and this lulled us into a state of obliviousness to imminent danger, so, like Odysseus and his companions, we strayed into the danger area. Alerted by my mother's shriek that something had happened inside the house, we dashed in, followed less eagerly by the young Reillys.

Polyphemus, awoken by raucous shouting outside his window, had emerged and was standing in the kitchen where the hapless Galatea had been preparing a meal on the kitchen table. Stark naked, his hair in mangled tresses, his face and legs gashed by wounds received during frequent falls, and looking as though he had not washed for a year, he stood screaming incoherently at the top of his considerable voice, and pounding the table with his knotted towel which, between spurts of water, sent the preparations for the meal flying in every direction. Both women were white with fear and, when we appeared, attempted to usher us children out of the room and close the door, but I stood transfixed. Here was the living proof of one of the most enigmatic and favourite illustrations in my uncle's old encyclopaedia, the Wild Man from Borneo. I had been fascinated by the small, out-of-focus image of a very hairy naked individual, and had scrutinized it with considerable interest, not really believing that such a person existed. Before I could further my research, my pullover was yanked and I was dragged out of the door. The madman did not pursue us but we could hear him bellowing and smashing things as we went back into the garden. After a while and with apologies for the lost meal (no reference was made to the culprit), goodbyes were said and we set off to catch the bus home.

As we sat in the bus, my mother said abruptly 'For God's sake', then she seemed to drift off, staring out the window until she continued, 'Let us *not* sit upon the ground and tell sad stories of the death of kings.' I wondered what was going on here? The problem with quotations (as I much later recognized) is that, unless previously heard and taken note of, you did not realize that it was a quote (more of the secret language of the adult world) and assumed that you might be expected to reply. 'Sit upon the ground', 'kings', had I missed something? And worse still, it might not be a straight quotation, but one adapted to the circumstances of the moment, as this one was.

My mother could neither ignore the incident, nor easily talk about it, so she fabricated a scenario in which what we had seen might reasonably be accommodated. On the return journey, she developed a migraine headache and when we arrived home we were dispatched to the kitchen and the maid's care, while she went to her bedroom. The following day she would be suffering acutely and we were warned not to disturb her. By the time she recovered, any opportunity to discuss the drama of Polyphemus's lair had conveniently passed. Yet the responsibility to explain or comment on the extraordinary scene bothered her: it could not just be ignored. She knew that it had been at the very least disturbing, if not utterly terrifying for my brother and me.

Eventually, when I had probably forgotten the incident, she brought up the subject of our visit to the Reillys, explaining that Polyphemus was ill, although there was no word for his difficult condition, but that he would recover, and it was best not to mention it to Grandmother, who knew the couple, since she might be worried and get upset. The formula of it being best not to speak of events to others neatly overcame the requirement to speak of them amongst ourselves. Duty was done in that Polyphemus's very public temper tantrum had been mentioned, while propriety was observed in that nothing of the slightest relevance had been said about it. Migraines or equivocation generally formed a handy substitute for the naming of spades, although, as my brother and I grew older, our mother became less reticent. My father, however, was, if the occasion arose, refreshingly direct and caustic in his observations, and did not hide behind subterfuges: 'A drunk, now intent on ruining his family, having utterly ruined himself' would have been a mild reference to the enraged one.

In due course, Polyphemus would come to his senses, or having being forced to do so, he had been dried out and returned to the world. Galatea accepted his remorseful return and their family life resumed some normalcy. Later, with Polyphemus transformed, they would come visiting and be greeted as the most genteel and familiar of my parents' friends. The anarchic vision of the demon's lair and his demented performance made it impossible for me to recognize the well-dressed and debonair reformed rake as the same person, so I correctly concluded that he must have a dual existence as two separate individuals.

Beyond the more local forbidden shops, an alleyway led downhill between small houses, to the next street where a distant relative of my mother's lived, and whom we periodically visited. The alley debouched on to the lower road through a dark arch in a terrace of small houses which contained another frowned-upon emporium. All these shops sold the same mundane fare: groceries for the locality, instantly predictable and reliable—bread and tea, tinned goods, jam, salt, sweets for children, jars of bull's eyes. The woman behind this counter might have been substituted for any of the others: busty, indolent, in a wrap-around blue spotted apron, intensely curious regarding any unknown face, even that of a child. Could there be a household in the immediate area that did not patronize her shop, an unacceptable thought? If so, the shopkeeper would be concerned to know who the strangers were, where exactly they lived. But visits to this particular shop were always a pretext, an opportunity, to see the madwoman who lived next door. Not that I was allowed to refer to this person in so dismissive and uncharitable a manner; just that she was 'disturbed'. We knew that she was far beyond the pale of any acceptable standard in eccentricity; she was indeed mad.

Positively Gothic in her strange dementedness and in the physicality of her emotional anguish, this woman was almost too visible. Her house was immediately identifiable by its unkemptness, in an era when keeping up appearances was the norm. Everything about it was decayed; paint flaking off the door and walls, windows cracked and broken. An abandoned-looking house was a rarity in our part of Cork. The madwoman lived in this house with her children, some tough-looking, ragged boys at whom it wouldn't be wise to look critically. The fact that set this woman apart was her entire separateness from the world around her. If out walking, she strode along the pavement, making no concessions to any other person who might be in her way. She proceeded at a panther-like pace, swiftly and purposefully, as though impelled by some driving force; a biblical prophet or one possessed. She was tall, as tatterdemalion as her sons, with hair streaming behind her in a witch's bush of matted tresses. More compelling than her stance and pace was her fixed stare, looking ahead at some invisible goal. But stranger and more alarming than her gaze was the position of her long, skeletally thin arms which, in angular gestures, gripped her chest and the small of her back as though she expected her body to suddenly explode. The fierceness with which she held herself in suggested something of the internal torment she was experiencing, and which presumably drove her to pace the streets as though attempting to escape from her demons. She terrified and fascinated me in equal measure, a figure of fun to the local children, as long as they were safely on the far side of the street. At some point she disappeared, or at least I saw her no more.

As I wandered through the great Post Impressionist exhibition at the Royal Academy in London in the late nineteen seventies, I was brought abruptly to a halt by a vivid and disturbing painting of a life-size figure of a woman. The painting suddenly emitted a piercing eldritch scream which caused me to back away and collapse on to a bench in the centre of the room. I looked around at the exhibition crowd to see if they had registered the scream. All were absorbed in studying the pictures with that particularly urbane quality of viewers in galleries in large cities, informed and knowledgeable, discussing each work with critical attention. Nobody looked at me, nor displayed any sense of having heard what I had—a distinct and anguished scream.

In the strangely surreal world of the Italian Futurists (those artists who in the first two decades of the twentieth century created a disquieting dream-world of the subconscious), the artist Giacomo Balla had captured a long-suppressed image from my childhood. The painting was of a tall, shabbily dressed woman striding through a doorway, one arm raised in front of her, close to her chest in an admonishing gesture, the other held stiffly by her side at a rigid angle, the palm open. Entitled *The Madwoman*, the image is of a person possessed, deranged, full of fearsome imaginings. The artist's intention was to depict an individual on the absolute fringes of sanity, some outcast from the norms of behaviour, part of a series of paintings which Balla called *Living Beings*. This was my madwoman, captured in paint in another country, forty years before I had seen her, yet hardly distinguishable from the figure in my memory. The horror and fascinated disquiet I had experienced as a child were here recreated. The scream the painting had emitted was in my head, as it instantly brought to my mind the recollection that the woman from the drab house used occasionally give voice to sudden high-pitched and disembodied screams while pacing in the street. The sight of Balla's *Madwoman* had evoked this long submerged childhood memory sufficiently vividly that when

I experienced the piercing scream in a quiet city art gallery, far from the place where I had originally encountered it so long before, I was hearing something long immured in my subconscious.

My mother's droll reordering of the real lives of the odd and eccentric baulked when confronted with the genuinely distressed, and she did not even like to be aware of this woman's existence, the naked and anarchic emotions were too disturbing for her to cope with. This type of dementia was beyond the territory of what she considered acceptable as a subject for humour. Her natural reticence was abetted by her husband's protective attitude to what she should know and what might be kept from her. In the last years of the war and its aftermath, when the daily revelations of Nazi atrocities were making newspaper headlines, my father would frequently manage to 'forget' to bring home the daily paper in order to shield her too-vivid imagination from some particularly distressing revelations. But this façade was one maintained by both of them since she might well have seen the very same censored headlines while on a journey to the shops during the day. So she knew he was deliberately concealing shocking information from her, and was content to acquiesce.

My recent close encounter with a fully alive and unquestionably hairy Wild Man from Borneo brought me back to my uncle's *Children's Encyclopaedia* where I had first become aware of this strangely fascinating individual. Disappointingly, the celebrated Wild Man had not been included in my own birth-and-baby-free encyclopaedia. I regretted his omission because the illustrations were so much clearer and would have given me an opportunity to study him more closely. I wondered if he had been tamed in the intervening years and was no longer considered sufficiently wild to be a valid subject for inclusion? This was another valuable lesson in the changeable veracity of fact. The possibility of censorship had even to be considered.

CHAPTER 19

My mother went through life without ever learning how to replace a light-bulb, believing firmly that God had created the male species principally for such useful tasks: an interpretation of the biblical narrative that has yet to receive widespread acceptance. She often said that 'a house needs a man' as one might say 'the grass needs cutting': men were one of those mundane aspects of creation without which nothing would work properly. Installing light-bulbs in their sockets was only a minor example of male facility. The aunt, who maintained a contrary view on most issues, did not share this infallible belief in the functional utility of all males of the species, particularly concerning her sister's husband. To the aunt, the male was a creature of limitless irritation—unreliable, dishonest and of questionable cleanliness. She liked to do all domestic tasks herself; had an effortless command of the light-bulb phenomenon, possessed well-stocked toolboxes, and knew how to use this equipment. She believed practical competence to be a prerequisite for being taken seriously. Not only did she regard my mother's indifference to physical utility as a clear indication of her dimwittedness, but also as a sign of downright perversity. In the latter opinion she may have been more close to the mark than she suspected.

By middle age, the enormity of the aunt's spite assumed a dominant force in her family encounters. Whether she had become slightly unbalanced, or was merely suffering from the internal pressure of sustained anger, her enmity for her family continued to fester, until it found final release on the occasion of my grandmother's funeral. By a destructive rejection of the cultural milieu in which she had been brought up, she settled scores with all the atavistic determination of an anarchist.

While the aunt viewed her sister's family with a combination of annoyance and contempt, her principal ire was directed at my father. To her frustration, he was largely impervious to her slights and snide comments, regarding her contempt as being beneath his. She visited at regular intervals and, failing to vex the master of the house, would attempt to antagonize anybody else whom she encountered there. My parents' friends were as much fair game as they were themselves as targets for her scorn, and it was a perpetual open-season for her troublemaking urges, invariably disguised behind a profusion of unwanted gifts and hearty conversation. She seemed unable to arrive without gifts, well chosen and expensive. This was the undesirable price to be paid for her society.

In the course of one of her visits, as she was waxing lengthily on the familiar topic of the idiocies of country town life in north Munster, and the utter impossibility of buying anything wearable in her local clothes shops, the front door-bell rang and Annie went to answer it. This was followed by some conversation and the admittance into the dining-room where the family was gathered, of Polyphemus, Galatea and their children. Since I had previously seen Polyphemus solely in demented Borneo mode, and subsequently he had been dried out and returned to the fold of his family and occupation, the transformation was total: the authentic wild-man look had been abandoned in favour of the assured and self-confident professional man, debonair and impeccably dressed. Knowing who they were and that this was a family with a dark secret to which no reference might be made, the aunt took it upon herself to humiliate them in a manner that appeared innocent, but was a calculated effort to drive them from the house. A humorous and caustic storyteller, she launched into a lively narrative about her town, punctuated by anecdotes concerning its more comic characters: the alcoholic doctor who misdiagnosed his patients, the tipsy curates who had to be carried home to their presbytery on doors, the dead-drunk postman delivering letters to the swans on the river, the town degenerates who drank in doorways and slept in the graveyard. Polyphemus listened to this coded parody of his own behaviour and blanched; Galatea glared, the children were silent. Abruptly they got up and left.

'Well,' said the aunt, 'what a nice family. A pity their visit was so brief!'

My brother sat deep in one of the dining room armchairs, absorbed by the book on his knees. The aunt, who had a genuine love of learning and reserved her admiration for bright children, could not but be impressed by his acumen, even if he were the child of her supposedly none-too-smart sister. After a child character in *Nicholas Nickleby*, the aunt had dubbed him the 'hinfant fernomenon' as a means of casting his genuinely considerable intellectual ability as something slightly comic, not to be praised or taken too seriously. Through her humour ran a strain of acidic ridicule. The fact that she would have been boasting to other teachers in her school if a child in one of her classes was as well informed as my brother was the type of contradiction in her general sense of approbation which she managed blithely to ignore. Her life was characterized by a similar lack of consistency in her attitudes. Allowances were made for the failings of the children of her friends, whereas no quarter was given to any child, even a Wittgenstein in embryo, if it had the bad taste to be the offspring of someone she considered inferior—in class, in education, in intelligence. There was an exclusivity in her sense of what was to be esteemed: the denizens of the buildings or their social equivalents in any city in the world dwelt forever beyond the pale of the educationally acceptable. The fact that my grandmother had praised my brother's 'BBC announcer's' reading capacity annoyed the aunt; she did not wish him to be acknowledged as a talented child, because then she would have been obliged to treat my mother's family with more respect than she was prepared to muster.

One of the aunt's few concessions to domestic harmony when visiting Windermere was to read poetry aloud to her nephews. Her taste was confined to the English classics and to Irish material of the Celtic Revival period. A gift of hers to the household had been a handsome edition of Wordsworth, with full-page illustrations of incidents from the more popular poems. Having read aloud from 'Lucy Gray' on a number of occasions, she periodically returned to this and other favourites, of which she gave effectively spirited readings. 'Lucy Gray' was illustrated by a picture of the distraught parents who have followed the child's steps in the snowbound landscape, only to see them cease at the centre of the footbridge from which she had fallen to her death. On picking up the book and leafing through it, the aunt discovered that this illustration had been altered. The footprints in the wet snow, which the illustrator had shown ending abruptly, had been neatly continued to the other side of the bridge—'improved' by another hand. In a fit of speechless fury, the aunt unwisely presented the book to my father as evidence of his sons' lack of respect for books. He stared at the picture and with a chuckle said, 'Well, that's very clever!', although he too would not have approved of books being drawn upon. The aunt moved her attention to the culprit, accusing my brother. He admitted the artwork to be his, adding that he had wished to save the life of poor Lucy, so he had completed her journey for her. For once, the aunt was confounded.

For me, the aunt made no pretence—she regarded me as irrevocably stupid, beyond the point of any redemption. The best she could say of me was that I was 'biddable', adding, as though for clarification, 'biddable, though simple'. This implied that even if nothing could be expected of me intellectually, at least I was obliging. The fact that I could be corralled in Rosenheim with the insalubrious Mrs Luby and whomever was the incumbent from the buildings, and apparently remain uncorrupted by the contact, indicated to her that I was useful and willing, even if I really comprehended nothing of the squalid life in her mother's house. Because my brother was challenging and capable of asking penetratingly intelligent questions, the aunt regarded him with a degree of suspicion—a boy (a bad start), her nephew (worse again), impertinent, too curious by far, all negatives. To me she was more tolerant, believing that, as an unchallenging simpleton, allowances had to be made. While my mother was not given to placing any credence in her sister's estimate of adults, she was intimidated by her authority as an experienced teacher, and regarded her knowledge of the young as being of some substance. The aunt led a curious divided existence: on the one hand, the scourge of her sister's family, while on the other, when amongst teaching colleagues, she was the soul of wit, a charming if acerbic conversationalist, well informed and interesting and, improbably, had the reputation of being an excellent and dedicated teacher. She specialized in English literature, in which she passionately believed, as though it constituted a form of religious belief.

On one occasion, I spent a summer holiday with the aunt in Cobh. In sardonic support of her mother's disdain, she insisted on referring to the town as 'Kob-h'. We stayed in a guesthouse run by some down-at-heel family whose grand mansion overlooked the harbour, its lawns shaded by immense conifers, its rooms filled with the pickings of generations of imperial bearers of the white man's burden; from India, Burma, China, West Africa. In the absence of a flourishing Empire and postings to somewhere east of Suez, they took in paying guests. We were both given enormous bedrooms from which the view stretched over the headlands guarding the harbour and far out to sea. In the hall in the morning a very ancient female was wheeled out in a wicker bath chair and left there for the day, her relationship to the family unexplained. Her wrinkled visage blended harmoniously with the Maori masks and Yoruba tribal figures. This was the period during which the aunt's propensity for reducing all those she regarded as comic or eccentric to a series of initials was given full rein. Thus our down-at-heel hosts became the d.a.h., and the ancient-of-days the a.o.d. It constituted a serious fall from grace not to instantly recognize or to confuse these references.

The trans-Atlantic liners that still plied the oceans visited Cobh (as the *Titanic* had done on her maiden voyage in 1912) as the last European port of call; to take on provisions, immigrants, and the gilded elite, last remnants of the carriage trade. Our holiday was spent visiting distant family connections, all of whom seemed to me to be irrevocably old and to live in houses indistinguishable from Grandmother's in the clutter of furnishings and ornaments occupying every room. These relatives or pseudo-family connections often, in defiance of reality, styled 'aunts', were a breed of indestructible spinsters, relics of sea captains, ships' surgeons and colonial administrators, whose lives had been spent abroad, and whose husbands now lay in the local graveyards, or where they had become 'safe in the arms of Jesus' on some dusty hillside in Poona or on the shores of the Great Lakes:

> *It dawns in Asia, tombstones show,*
> *And Shropshire names are read;*
> *And the Nile spills her overflow,*
> *Beside the Severn's dead.*

The lines might, with slight topographical alterations—'…And Kob-h names are read…'—have been written for the lost spouses of this doughty tribe of women whom we visited dutifully, the exact relevance of each explained in advance by the aunt, their relationship or otherwise to my grandparents. I was expected to maintain all this information as a reference system to our complicated connections in the locality.

Rowed by an ex-seaman whom we had hired at the pier, we made short trips around the harbour on sunny days and, when the opportunity arose, boarded the liners at anchor off the town, to spend an afternoon imagining ourselves outward-bound for New York. The aunt hated the sea, distrusted men generally, the seaman as the man of the moment in particular, and disliked being far from *terra firma*. Incarcerated in a land-locked country town for most of the year, she felt that sea air and boating were penances necessary for the full relishing of a coastal holiday. Moreover, her boating trips would give grist to accounts of her holiday when she returned home. Remembering Grandmother's romantic notions of boating in the days when the harbour was busy with naval fleets, and her image of lazily dipping one's fingers in the water, I followed her description. Leaning over the side of the boat, I trailed my hand in the pure green coldness of the deep, relishing the chilliness of the water. The aunt gave a loud screech and told me to remove my hand from 'that filthy water'. The boatman nearly lost one of his oars and looked around, expecting me to have fallen overboard. I withdrew my hand and refrained from further emulation of an Edwardian miss, while the seaman glared at the aunt's abuse of his natural element. After this incident, we had to find a new boatman because that one refused to take us out again.

In a gesture of magnanimity when we arrived, the aunt had presented me with a book so that I 'might look at the pictures' if I was unable to read an entire page. I took it to my room and perused it. The story was interesting; I read it in a few evenings after I had been sent to bed, while the aunt was occupied downstairs interrogating the d.a.h. hosts. On being questioned a few days later as to whether or not I had looked at the book, I replied that I had finished reading it.

The aunt became incensed and shouted 'You lie' and rushed to my bedroom and returned with the book. She wielded the volume like the images of Martin Luther in the steel engravings in the hall, quelling all dissent, and appealed to the d.a.h.s to witness the outrage of 'a boy who lied'. The pale and sheepish husband and wife were summoned from the servantless kitchen where they had been doing the washing-up after the guests' breakfast, and stood in the hall like children waiting to be scolded; the a.o.d. looked on with her expressionless tribal mask, clucking inaudibly. The aunt brandished the book and, glaring at me as though I had been found guilty of high treason, flung it on the tiled floor. 'That', she said 'is the last book I will ever buy for you or your lying and ungrateful family.' I attempted to protest and to explain that I had indeed enjoyed the story, and had read it all. Never for a moment doubting the correctness of her assumption, she picked up the book, handed it to me and commanded 'Read!'

As I did so, slowly, with the faltering pace of one unaccustomed to reading aloud, and unsure of the pronunciation of words recognized but never heard spoken and probably not fully understood, she realized her mistake—I could read competently and had evidently completed the book. With a cry of annoyance at having been wrong, and having shown herself as unjust before the d.a.h.s, she stomped up the stairs to her room, returning within a few minutes with her coat and hat on. She marched out of the house, and down the hill towards the town, leaving me with the book in my hand, gaping after her. She had left without saying a word, in contrast to the avalanche of instructions normally showered on me if left alone.

Mr d.a.h. looked at his wife and smiled encouragingly as though the embarrassing scene they had witnessed were a pardonable eccentricity on the aunt's behalf.

'Well, then', he said, 'we might have a game of croquet if the weather holds', giving a conspiratorial tap to the hall barometer. 'Come, first we will have cocoa and some scones.'

Before following them into the kitchen, I carefully deposited my now poisoned book on a shelf in the hall, inserted between the po-faced volumes of Wilson's *Views of Seats* and Layard's *Nineveh*, where it would remain long after we had returned to the city, presided over by the spectres of empires past and the a.o.d. While my reading prowess did not dislodge the *hinfant fernomenon* from his pre-eminent position as the child genius of the household, the aunt ceased to regard me as an irrevocable imbecile and never again made disparaging remarks at my expense.

CHAPTER 20

If my father possessed the gift of enduring friendships with his colleagues and maintained close and amicable relations with his brother-officers, it was in a spirit of camaraderie rather than any shared sense of male bonding or anything suggestive of masculine supremacy. He enjoyed the company of men, but was a ladies man when not ensconced in the officers' mess at his barracks. Years after his death, I met the father of a school friend who had been one of the junior officers when I was a child in Windermere. This now senior officer referred to jokes my father had told in the officers' mess twenty years before, which were still recounted to later generations. Since I lacked the gumption to request an example of these legendary paternal witticisms, I can only speculate on their nature.

He liked to tell complicated stories where the listener's full attention was demanded. If interrupted, he might (like Grandmother) decline to continue, although more because he was obstinate than because of any sense of injured pride. His more experienced listeners were loth to go away with half a story and remained mute. Firm to the point of obduracy, he began telling a story to my mother while they were honeymooning in Versailles but, being a novice in the ways of bloody-minded males, she intruded some abstract concern, unrelated to his narration. Fifteen years later she was still requesting the end of the story, while he remained adamant and refused to oblige. The mess-room stories, the long silver-topped ebony cigarette holder, the languid smoke rings were all of a piece. The stories were elongated like those of a *seanchaí* to unreasonable length as a form of performance art, and were conceived to establish a presence. Like Scheherazade, he would continue the next day (unless interrupted).

My mother's friends were of two groups. The first were those with whom she had been to college; these were enduring relationships that might have been colour-coded as to education and upbringing: beige was a favourite hue, the cashmere cardigan a uniform. The second category consisted of those more chance acquaintances, mostly neighbouring housewives with children whom she ran into while out of doors. With some of the latter group she formed relationships, from which, no sooner were they established, than she sought to extract herself. Unfortunately, she lacked the will or forthrightness to simply drop anybody. Mrs Peabody, who lived down the street from Windermere, became firmly attached to my mother and took to calling frequently. At first she remained for half-an-hour, but later the visits expanded to occupy an entire afternoon, secure in the knowledge that her own maid was attending to her children. A characteristic of many of these local acquaintances was that my mother seemed to gravitate effortlessly towards those with whom she had least in common, but who were gifted with an endless capacity for irrelevant small-talk. When my father arrived home for the third day in succession and found Mrs Peabody ensconced in the drawing room sipping tea, he became irritated because he could see that this was not a flourishing relationship. His wife, visibly showing the strain of hours of aimless chit-chat, was either too kind or too polite to stand up and say, 'Well, I won't be keeping you from your tasks, Mrs Peabody. So kind of you to call', or some similar prompt to edge the unwelcome visitor towards the door. She clearly needed assistance in disengaging the guest. My father opened his assault with a gambit designed to dislodge the visitor from her perch.

'Fire brigade outside your house, Mrs Peabody. I trust it wasn't anything too serious, no damage done, lives lost? I passed an ambulance as I came round the corner!'

Mrs Peabody erupted from her chair and was out the front door at speed, her coat and hat half on as she ran down the street in expectation of catastrophe, looking for the non-existent fire tender, the imaginary ambulances ferrying away her incinerated children. It did not take more than a few such encounters with my father for Mrs Peabody or other women to get the point – when making social calls, they should be well gone from the premises before the husband returned.

There was something in my mother's makeup which constantly got her into trouble, a formidable character-flaw long exploited by her bullying older sister, and which frequently caused her acute unhappiness. She possessed a hypnotic attraction for toxic friendships, and attracted to her women who assumed that she needed guidance in the stormy path of life, and proceeded to intrude on her private world. Repeatedly, my father had to ride in to rescue her from the latest 'friendship', coming over the top of the hill like a lone US cavalryman with sabre drawn. These do-gooders attempted to save her soul; show her a better way to make almond paste, had an improved recipe for silver-polish, or had solved the 'servant problem'. One of these women attempted to enlighten my mother as to how the hardworking and obliging Annie might be induced to do more work for less money. My mother did not really suffer from any of these problems but was too well-mannered to suggest to her advisers that she was getting on fine with her maid and that her soul was not a topic for public discussion. So she submitted to torture of various opinionated and garrulous individuals with time on their hands. Having once admitted them to her home, she had no idea how they might be got rid of or prevented from calling again. Either these women had an abrasive encounter with my father which hastened their departure, or they eventually realised that my mother was impervious to suggestion, mouthing platitudes or offering tea while keeping her own counsel and waiting for them to leave. Herself immune from the corrosive power of jealousy, she seemed like a lightning conductor in attracting the envious spite of others.

Another of her long-term unfriendly friends was Mrs Dalhousie, whom she found attractive on account of her physical resemblance to Grandmother when young. Mrs Dalhousie was tall and striking, wearing her auburn hair in precisely the same style as Grandmother, great tiers of braids and rolls of hair, pinioned on the top of her head in defiance of gravity. She was tall and erect and possessed the dignity of a bygone age. Some elder of her circle had remarked of her as a young woman that she would make a fit wife for a Viceroy, a post not so long abolished that it had passed from public memory as the apogee of social distinction, and she never quite got over the image of herself dispensing favours on the lawns of the Viceregal Lodge in the Phoenix Park. *Noblesse oblige* became one of her favourite expressions, as though the aura of the Park had granted her access to some form of aristocratic ancestry. It is unclear whether she consciously modelled herself on some obsolete manner of the past or was a pioneering style victim, but it is more likely that the decision was a conscious one. Mrs Dalhousie frequently invited my mother to come to her house for an evening, which, after much prevarication, she eventually agreed to do. These were not visits where husbands were welcome. Her own spouse would be banished from the house, and my father was merely expected to deliver and collect his wife, not penetrating beyond the doorstep.

The evening's ritual consisted of preamble, denunciation, accusation and proof. The preamble over tea and cakes would be confined to a pleasant exchange of chat: novels read, films seen, the current news, the doings of their respective neighbourhoods, mutual friends and casual acquaintances. Mrs Dalhousie then expanded on her denunciation. This consisted of a diatribe on the state of the nation, the idiocy of the current government, the decline in service among shop assistants, the price of tea. Comment on the absence of culture in local civic figures was followed by further invective. Public life could always be relied upon to provide her with an infinite list of stupidities with which to harangue my mother, as though she were personally culpable for the low standards in national affairs. Having exhausted the minutiae of social shortcomings and politics, she entered her main topic—my mother's inadequacies as a parent—a subject on which Mrs Dalhousie held trenchant views: the accusation had begun. The catalyst of her critique was always the superlative behaviour of her own son, held up as a paragon of young manhood. Mrs Dalhousie, having met my brother and me in town with our mother, appeared to have spent the encounter scrutinizing our manners, our fingernails and our knees, evaluating our capacity to stand still while the adults conversed, never any child's forte. Naturally we fell short on all counts and many others. As she expanded, my mother retreated, never venturing to attack or criticize the junior Dalhousie, no more odious or virtuous than her own sons. By the time my father collected her, she would be pale and silent, resolving never to be enticed again into that house, until six months later she succumbed to another invitation to the spider's lair.

Mrs Dalhousie's problem was that she had, in her own view, married beneath herself and unquestionably beneath the horizon of the Viceregal Lodge. It would have been folly for her to attempt to denigrate the husbands of her friends whose professions or education granted them a secure social position. She concentrated instead on condemning their children as a means of assuaging her own sense of failure in having married a shop-walker in one of the city's department stores. Doubtless, Mr Dalhousie presented a very romantic figure when first encountered, with his polished manner and impeccably tailored suits.

That, unfortunately, was all he brought to the table, and it could be rather hard to endure a suave manner at breakfast-time. A shop-walker was a significant, though poorly paid, role in the better-class shops of the day. The walker literally walked around the shop floor, nodding to the carriage trade, being charming to regular customers, ushering significant persons to or from the entrance—he did not actually do anything else. The closest form of employment to the shop-walker was the undertaker, except that the latter was not encouraged to smile at his customers. Shop-walker and undertaker moved similarly without haste, gliding between points and never becoming ruffled.

Mrs Dalhousie's undoing was that she fell for the glide, not recognizing that no other talents accompanied this elegant accomplishment. With a son and a suavely dull husband quite lacking in ambition, she sought easy targets for her barely contained anger at the world. My mother offered herself as sacrificial victim.

Occasionally my mother rallied and engaged in a counterattack. These initiatives were so styled that only the more astute were likely to realize that they were being lampooned. She responded to the *noblesse oblige* syndrome with an outbreak of *reductio ad absurdum*. Her lifelong interest in etymology frequently came to her rescue and she launched an attack on Mr Dalhousie's mobile profession, never alluded to by Mrs Dalhousie. She closed on this target.

'*To walk* or *walking* is of course a very interesting word. I was thinking the other day about its usage—you will find this most compelling. I looked it up in *The Concise Oxford*.'

Mrs Dalhousie was suddenly afflicted by a painful cough.

'*Progress by lifting or setting down each foot in turn.* Isn't that good? But you will like the rest from the OED much better: *never having both feet off the ground at the same time.* Isn't that just perfect? Imagine.' Warming to her satire on the gliding one, she accelerated into her own glide.

'And in the instance of quadrupeds, *go with the slowest gait, always having at least two feet on the ground at once.* Now wouldn't Mr Dalhousie find that fascinating, although not a quadruped himself of course!'

'And then there is also *perambulate*, what a gorgeous word that is. Do you think that Mr Dalhousie perambulates? I suspect that he does in his official capacity. I wonder what Dr Johnson had to say in his *Dictionary* about *walk* and *walking*? *Sir, a man who is tired of walking...*', she broke off, recognizing that her parody of the good lexicographer was only getting her further mired in Mrs Dalhousie's enmity, for which there would be retribution at some future date. But once started on this fanciful line of thought, she found it difficult to extract herself, one idea inevitably giving birth to another.

' "Will you walk a little faster?' said a whiting to a snail, 'There's a porpoise...".'

On the journey home in the car, my father made his opinion known. The sight of my mother's tight expression and giddy replies were quite enough to convince him that the visit had not been a success. He was familiar with his wife's vacillating responses, to either be humiliated or to engage in some surreal dialogue, the latter generally received by her listeners as being deliberately offensive.

'Why do you insist on visiting that delusional dowager?' he asked, 'She doesn't like you, or the boys. All she ever succeeds in doing is upsetting you. What rubbish did she come out with this time?' My mother, a willing victim, had no desire to blacken the reputation of her accuser, and refrained from itemizing the well-directed barbs of criticism of her children, so she remained silent. This he took as evidence that Mrs Dalhousie had probably been condemning him as well.

'All that husband of hers ever does is trot around the shop with his imbecilic smirk, kow-towing to women in furs and diamonds. He is probably a faggot. Little wonder she's frustrated.' To this proposition my mother had only one response: she burst into tears, now regretful of her slander of the perambulatory trade.

'So what did you say to her?'

'I defined *walk* and *walking* from the OED!'

He smiled broadly, revving the engine with satisfaction, and drove on.

Whether my mother had very bad taste in choosing friends, or just very bad luck, many of her friendships belonged to the troubled variety of one-sided battles, from which she frequently emerged disturbed and crushed. The social situation in which she was at her best was in mixed assemblies of the captains and their queens, where female spite and jealousies would not be directed at her, and her capacity for repartee and apt literary allusions could excel. This was her style, much admired by her husband, who lacked a literary education or a polished vocabulary. He loved to see her blossom in company and became irritated at her entanglements with people whom he regarded as stupid, vicious and not worth consideration. He was quick to evaluate situations and people, but was not blessed with her kindness of heart and unwillingness to judge harshly of others. Her inner world and creative fantasies concerning strangers were clearly more palatable that the poisonous reality of some of her acquaintances.

To everything that concerned her, my mother brought a practiced vagueness as a defence against the realities of the world, in contrast to her husband, who was forever attempting to regulate her affairs, and to discourage her involvements with destructive individuals. His sense of there being a pattern to events was offended by the arbitrariness of her judgments. Used to the organizing of men and munitions, he had respect for method, and involved himself with the theories of wars and their manipulation. 'Tactics' was the phrase he often used – 'we must consider our tactics', as though the Dalhousie offensive might be counteracted by some strategic redeployment of forces.

Although she had never set foot on English soil, my mother's speech was as a mark of Cain: clipped vowels, precise diction and modulated tones broadcast the wrong message to a population to whom the acme of racial purity was to be descended from seven generations of tillers of the soil. The Ireland of her time esteemed the demotic above all, the 'colleens' and the 'sturdy children' promoted as the supreme national aspiration. Unable to fit in on an aural plane, she drifted further into her own realm of internal emigration. She was incapable of purchasing a loaf of bread without sounding as if she had emerged from a Swiss finishing-school for young ladies, so she made her voice another vehicle to keep the prying world at bay.

The recently developed science of time-and-motion-study had attracted my father's attention and he liked to put these new theories into use, practising on his army transport corps or his family. Realizing that his wife would not respond to an exacting organization of her activities, which tended to be intuitive, he concentrated on his sons and Annie. In order to improve Annie's domestic performance, he came and sat in the kitchen, observing her work methods and taking notes, to the embarrassment of the maid and to my mother's considerable annoyance. She regarded the workings of the kitchen as her business and did not welcome his advice on how many motions the maid needed to turn on the taps or lift the kettle. The field in which he initially scored some partial success was Annie's washing-up technique. This consisted of piling everything to be washed in a disordered and precarious heap and gradually working her way down from the top, with the occasional crash as something slipped from the draining board on to the floor. Under the new dispensation, all items had to be sorted beforehand, coded according to shape, size and materials, allocated individual spaces appropriate to their contours, and processed in a rhythmical and repetitive order, being stacked afterwards for drying in a complementary manner. Once the method had been established and perfected, it was to be followed without deviation. Naturally, his search for domestic order was thwarted by the opposition of ingrained habit. The amiable Annie, having 'Yes sir'd and 'No sir'd throughout her induction process, proceeded to do her jobs just as she had always done them. With my brother and myself, my father had a more lasting success, pointing out that putting on one sock and shoe, then one's underpants and shirt, followed by another sock, then tying the laces of the first shoe, lacked logic as a method. This proved to be a lasting lesson in the way things should be done and left a lifetime of excellent methodology to his sons. From the activities of the kitchen he had to retire, advanced theory undermined by historic precedent.

Blitz was not the family dog in the sense that some dogs are, loved by all members of the family, a collective pet, fed by whomever happens to remember. Blitz was solely my father's dog, and responded to him with the certainty of an enduring relationship. When, during the war, my father occasionally cycled at weekends, taking one or other of his sons on the child's seat on the crossbar of his bicycle, the dog invariably came along. Although a photograph exists of my mother, as a young woman, cycling, she never did so in my recollection, and did not join these excursions. The cycle journey consisted of some major circuit of the city's outskirts, lasting a few hours and occupying an entire afternoon. Blitz happily ran beside the rider or made forays into adjoining fields and ditches. Unfortunately he lacked that essential doggy trait of having a sense of direction and so he frequently got lost. Either we would return disconsolately from a cycle ride without the dog, or we would have spent hours going in circles around the spot where he had last been seen: in and out of fields and up and down byroads trying to locate him. Blitz eventually would be discovered happily devouring a rabbit he had killed. He also wandered away from the house, leading to lengthy absences. These departures involved putting advertisements in the local newspaper, 'Kerry Blue terrier missing, answers to the name of Blitz', with the improbable result of a week later some farmer writing from thirty miles away, announcing that he had the dog in question and would expect to be paid for its upkeep. My father muttered darkly about kidnapping and extortion, but rescued Blitz from his latest exile, reluctantly parting with a five-pound note to his host. Sometimes the dog returned of his own accord, but more frequently his absences resulted in an expedition to some unlikely location where he had gone exploring and had forgotten the way home.

Blitz was a beautiful and friendly dog—his tightly curled coat, pristine and well-trimmed—and just the sort of domestic pet who might attract the attention of a prowling dog thief. My father's belief was that the dog was too trusting and was being lured away by strangers. He also suspected that some delivery-boy or local tradesman might be on the look-out for stealable animals, and eventually became convinced that kidnapping was being practiced. Following Blitz's periodic disappearance from our back garden, and the passage of a week when he failed to reappear, a letter would arrive in the post. This was usually written on a thin sheet of lined paper, evidently torn from a child's school exercise copy, correctly addressed to my father but in a hand unused to letter writing:

> *Sir,*
> *There is a dog on me land which I bayleev is yourn an*
> *I hev bean to great costs in its feeding. Five poun will*
> *suffice for me ixpinses.*
> > *Faithfully yourn,*
> > *Danl Cotter, fearmer.*

How the ingenious Mr Cotter might have traced Blitz's residence (unless stolen to order) remained unexplained when my father arrived at the address in the countryside. Divine intervention was implied: God being good and his ways inscrutable. After a repetition of these episodes, my father proffered a pound and mentioned that the police would be involved the next time Blitz found himself lodging with the hospitable Mr Cotter.

CHAPTER 21

The first person, indeed probably the sole individual I remember positively disliking or even hating as a child, was German. He was the first German person I had ever met, the first and only foreigner I had come across by the age of seven, living in war-isolated Ireland where any foreigner was regarded with suspicion as a probable spy. Karl Weber was also seven, slightly taller than me, painfully thin and with a guarded expression in which I registered something unknown and troubling. I was a plump and well-fed boy, and the sight of this skinny blond stranger with almost colourless eyes, a terrible haircut and outlandishly peculiar clothes, struck me with unease. I disliked him even before I had met him, since my parents described him to me as being in need of my affection.

'You will like Karl', they announced.

'We must try to be kind to him and make him welcome. You might like to give him some of your toys.' Doubt turned to horror at this latter pronouncement, only to be followed by a statement that I recognized as the death-knell of my frivolous life, the end of carefree days.

'He is one of the starving children from Europe.' The starving Armenians and my mother's convoluted rigmarole in response to my questions had been discomforting enough. Now we were to have tough and starving children from the slums of Europe eating potatoes off our doorstep!

Throughout my childhood, the war hovered as a constant although distant presence, something adults would stop speaking about when children were around, then after a few minutes, forget themselves and continue. So while quietly playing with my toys, I listened intently to the adult conversation of troop movements, invasion plans, battles, bombings and concentration camps. I overheard much, although in factual terms it meant nothing to me. I had no concept of who the Germans were, other than that they were not us. Who we were consisted of my family, Grandmother's household, our neighbours, the people on the BBC and Irish radio, and inside the gramophone, all of whom could be considered familiar. Beyond these close confines, everybody and everything was unknown. The war was happening elsewhere, the British were on our side, or perhaps we were on theirs; the Germans were the enemy. As soon as the war was over, we were to be visited by an enemy child to whom I was expected to give my toys, the reason for which I failed to understand.

Karl Weber was staying with a host family who were childless and probably understood little about children: the husband was a brother officer of my father's. They spoke no German and, when he arrived, Karl spoke no English. He too was seven years old; far from his war-ravaged home and from his family, trying to cope with a strange tongue, the language of his enemies and in, for all he knew, the land of the enemy. He was one of the German children facing near starvation at home, who had been brought to Ireland in the aftermath of World War II—a refugee and a survivor of the last terrible years of the war in Berlin. When his proud and nervous foster-parents brought him to visit us for the first time, his accomplishments were paraded. After a few days in his new home, he could count to fifty in English in a heavily accented voice. Moreover, he could dress himself without assistance and had impeccable table-manners, although he never looked you in the eye.

All this admired performance was too much for me. I could not count or spell with any accuracy, and had an even more hazy sense of learning as some form of performance, where recitation of things learned was regarded as a social accomplishment. Karl knew the entire alphabet and delivered it unintelligibly and at speed in German. As his English improved, I felt intimidated by the parroted sentences, as though they were in a scarcely disguised foreign tongue, which in fact was just what they were. I felt that I had no accomplishments to demonstrate to this hateful German boy, and that it was unfair of my parents and their friends to expect me to be pally with the enemy, whom we seemed to have been fighting for my entire life, particularly an enemy with approved table-manners.

For a number of weeks Karl's hosts had failed to persuade him to leave off the garments in which he had arrived, and to put on the new clothes that they had bought for him. It was months before he was prepared to even try on some of the new clothes. He insisted on always having some element of the clothes in which he had come as part of his outfit. He never explained this reluctance, just uttered an emphatic and scowling 'Nein!' His jacket and short trousers looked as if they had been made from an adult's by cutting them down, and this was doubtless the case: the colour and fabric were suspiciously similar to those of my father's military uniform. The style and cut of his clothes was so very obviously different from what was the local norm; the home-knit Fairisle pullovers and box-pleated overcoats which we wore, that the German-ness of them made me uneasy. It was as though his clothes proved beyond doubt that he was the enemy, nothing less than a child spy. There had been talk of spies for years and now we had one visiting us. It just was not fair. I couldn't understand why my parents, normally so sensible and protective, were fraternizing in this treacherous manner, as though unaware of the enemy within, considering all the talk of war with which I had grown up and the constant warning of the need to be vigilant. Even though Karl was only my own age, I was convinced that he was a spy, sent to Ireland for some sinister purpose.

After numerous visits from Karl and his host family, it was obvious that I was not prepared to be friendly to the refugee, or to share my toys with him. I did not like him, or anything about his accomplishments, with which I could not compete. When 'the Webers' arrived, Karl was sent with me to my bedroom to play. This involved a ritual whereby he would, in his faulty but increasing vocabulary, exclaim about my toys and in particular anything new. With formal grace he would compliment me on any new possession and play with it himself while I watched.

'This is good', was his usual guttural response. 'Good.'

He and I reached an unspoken arrangement of mutual disregard; he played on one side of the room, I on the other. We neither talked, fought, nor played together. When we were called downstairs, we came together as though we had been jointly involved in a diverting game since this was what both pairs of adults expected. The admiration which my parents expressed for the German boy increased as his command of English grew and made his good manners more apparent. He was clever and clearly understood that his status as a Berlin war orphan was enhanced by his ability to communicate. However, in answer to my parents' questions about his life before his arrival with us, he was silent. He declined to answer any request for information as to siblings, parents, school or other family matters. This probably represented his way of coping with the dislocation and isolation of being wrenched from his family, with whom he could not now communicate, into the strangeness of his new surroundings. He just put the past out of reach of the prying questioners in his new world.

Karl Weber never smiled or laughed; he was always solemn and serious, speaking slowly as though with extreme effort, like an old person. His manner of talking reminded me of my grandmother's laboured speech and I often wondered if he were secretly also an old person, who for some mysterious purpose (spying?) had been encased in an enemy child's body. Certainly, his lack of a spirit of fun made me dread his visits, and if I had not been prejudiced against him already, this, as a jolly and unserious child, would have given me ample reason. As we played separately in my bedroom, he would make oblique references to what he referred to as 'those people'. It took me some time to realize that he was talking about his host family, and I began to understand that on some level he was sharing with me as a 'friend' the fact that he disliked the couple who were caring for him. Sometimes his negativity concerning 'those people' was positively vehement. 'Those people are stupid; they want to adopt me. I want to go home. Those people are not nice.' These statements, no more than any other part of Karl's conversation, failed to reveal anything about him or his hosts, beyond the fact that he was unhappy and wished to return to Germany. His hosts continued to dote on him, oblivious of his antagonistic response.

'Those people want me to be an Irish.' He stamped his foot emphatically. 'I am not an Irish.'

Furthermore, he took things. A childhood that in time paralleled mine, but was spent in a state of perilous existence amongst the dark cellars and ruins of Berlin, had no doubt helped him to hone his survival skills. When his life was threatened on a daily basis by starvation in the final years of the war and its aftermath (in fact the only world he had known), he must have learned to be self-reliant. Karl evidently was not brought up as a street urchin, but he may have had to live as one. He pocketed small things of mine: well-chosen small toys, a piece of a Meccano set, or a particular glass marble. I never saw him take anything, but when I challenged him once on the disappearance of one of my prize possessions, he responded with his usual solemn expression and said, 'It is gone. A pity', which did not help to convince me of his innocence. So admired was Karl by his foster-parents, and by my parents as well, that suggestions that he was light-fingered would have been ill received. I never could mention the matter to my parents, but when he visited, which he did on a weekly basis, I followed him like a shadow, yet never detected him in the act of putting something in his pocket. My guilt at failing my parents' standards of hospitality and their seeing themselves as offering a helping-hand to the defeated Germany, prevented Karl's faults from being discussed.

The proof that he was a child-spy came in a manner that I felt my parents could not possibly ignore, yet they remained oblivious of the evidence. On a visit to a nearby seaside resort, we were joined by the Webers. This was the first time that I had seen Karl's feet without shoes and socks. They were deformed, smaller than they should have been for his age, the toes retracted in a painful-looking manner. Although the state of his feet in no way inhibited his ability to run on the sand, I remembered one of the captains' pronouncements on the Lord Haw Haw/Francis Stuart radio talks, that 'only some twisted individual would broadcast for the enemy'. Here was my proof, but my parents could not see it. When I questioned my mother about Karl's feet, she produced an altogether more prosaic explanation. She said that he had grown up wearing shoes, which, owing to the wartime scarcity of leather, were far too small for him. This had retarded their natural growth. I, of course, knew the true explanation.

Then Karl's foster-family was transferred to another part of the country and his visits became less frequent. Some months later I overheard my mother discussing 'the Webers' with one of her friends. The phrase 'that insufferable German boy' stuck in my mind. Although I had no idea what the adjective meant, I understood from the tone of her voice that the remark was not complimentary. Getting beyond the point at which his hosts felt some culpability for the bombing of his home, and his own sense of aggrieved dislocation, yet understanding that this exile was temporary, did not make it any easier for Karl to love and be loved. There was too much at stake, which his hosts understood, but with which he did not have the capacity to come to terms. When Karl eventually returned to Berlin after eighteen months in Ireland, he could speak faultless Irish-accented English; I could count stumblingly up to twenty in German. He departed as he had arrived, unsmiling and with a solemn and penetratingly suspicious stare. He was no longer a stick-figure, but the aura of anxiety, which had hung over him throughout his stay in Ireland, remained with him.

Shortly after Karl's repatriation, as though one step ahead of the invading army in a war-movie, my brother and I were taken from our beds, late at night, carried to the car in rugs and put back to sleep on the back seat. In an ordered world, such an excursion was sufficiently unusual to be a cause of alarm. There were no pursuing panzers: in June 1948 Éire had declared itself to be the Republic of Ireland, and fireworks over the river Lee at midnight celebrated the event. The resultant *Feu de Joie* was a celebration of many things; principally an escape from our collective past, from the British Commonwealth, from the war, from history itself. A new dawn, a thousand-year Gaeldom, was promised. In awe, I stood amongst dark crowds of strangers on the quays of the river and watched the fireworks in the sky. I had no idea what it was about, nor did I particularly care, as long as I was with my family and knew that we could go home again soon. The meaning of public celebrations to one with no historical or even contemporary concept of nationhood was merely a selection of words and slogans, none of which I grasped.

The fact that, when a few years younger, my father had discovered that I had no idea whether we were living in England or Ireland, nor that the 'we' of the war conflict did not actually represent 'us' but the neighbouring island, our historic and traditional enemy, had been a cause of incredulous amusement to him and his colleagues. Perhaps the nature of my dislocation was the motive for our attending this event, in order to dislodge my vagueness as to whom we were and where we were actually living: from now on I was to be a part of the surrounding mass of anonymous people shuffling in the cold.

CHAPTER 22

From the fireplace in the bedroom a tube, some three feet long, projected into the room at an angle. It ended in a wide shallow funnel that was supported on the wire-mesh fireguard. The bright copper funnel was finished by a brass rim and looked as if it might have been part of a ship or an airplane-fitting of some kind: evidently it had been drafted into this new improved function and belonged in the garage with my father's collection of useful things, scavenged from redundant military equipment. The opportunity of turning the gun-turret of an armoured car into a dog-kennel would have appealed to him, as would any other practical re-use of redundant military matériel.

From the aperture issued a dense, strong-smelling cloud of whitish vapour, billowing out like plumes from a steam-ship funnel. It rose towards the ceiling, reminding me of the illustration of Aladdin's lamp and the smoke out of which the genie appeared. I sat up in bed in my corner by the window, while in the far corner between the fireplace and the wall my brother lay in his bed, reading. Gradually the vapour became a cloud, and in time my brother became less visible until he was just a shape, indistinguishable from the bulk of his bed. Then he disappeared altogether. The fireplaces in all the rooms had cast iron grates with, at one or both sides, a swivel-attachment that could swing over the fire and support a kettle. On one of these small platforms a kettle was resting, the end of the tube set over its spout. It was from this cauldron that the devil's brew was issuing.

My brother and I were ill and confined to bed. Ill with what? Something bronchial I imagine. The contents of the kettle were an infusion intended to relieve respiratory problems. As the kettle simmered over the fire, the fug billowed out into the room until it was entirely occupied with fumes, similar to the view from an aeroplane when passing through clouds, a dense and impenetrable woolly whiteness. No longer able to even see his book, my brother started calling across the void and we were enjoying the sensation of being in a familiar place transformed by the sudden and inexplicable intrusion of low cloud formations.

Whatever game or joke was engaging us, our voices continued to rise and eventually my father could be heard coming upstairs. He entered the room and I could feel his footfalls on the floor and then hear his voice, dulled by the enveloping cotton wool of the vapour, although he remained invisible. Suddenly he began to sing and, like a foghorn at sea, his voice carried through the gloom, disembodied and strange. What he sang was probably one of the popular arias from opera, Rodolfo's song to Mimi in *La Bohème*, 'Your tiny hand is frozen, let me warm it into life' or the chorus of the Hebrew Slaves from Verdi's *Nabucco*. When he sang, which was not often, and more frequently in the car than at home, arias from Puccini or Verdi were his favourites. Here, invisible to his children, he broke uninhibitedly into song, probably more vigorously and spontaneously than he might have done otherwise. I sat in my bed, breathing in the mist of what was most probably Friar's Balsam (a cure for throat infections or possibly tonsilitis) while he sang the male part of one of the most beautiful love duets in all opera. Then my mother's step and voice could be heard, urging him to stop, since it was bad for our throats, although it was he who was singing while we had not uttered a note. When the vapour thinned, he emerged like the genie into full view, but vanished again by abruptly going out the door, leaving us to our Balsamic heaven.

The Balsam was among my mother's arsenal of patent or old wives' remedies, generally unsanctioned by the medical profession. Despite the fact that she had boundless respect for the medical profession and for our family GP, a man with an oleaginous bedside manner and a well-developed sense of his own worth, she liked to play safe. She baked folklore and science in equal measure by using traditional juju-spells, in tandem with the best of modern medicine. In order to contain the fumes, a sheet was hung over the door and another over the window, reducing the draughts and creating an atmosphere so pungent and soporific that, following the unseen concert performance, we fell asleep, continuing to inhale the white fluffy cloud. Some days later, we both had our tonsils removed in a local hospital, so there may after all have been method in her medicine.

Clearly my mother had an enthusiasm for infusions, and I recollect numerous occasions when I was required to sit at a table with my head under a tent-like towel, my face suspended in the near-dark over a steaming bowl of sweet-smelling liquid that was guaranteed to cure the current affliction. It might have been Camomile or the same Balsam differently presented, or some other herbal concoction altogether, such as an infusion to improve the hair, a remedy for head-lice or a cure for an earache. Minor illnesses seemed to dog our household, although I suspect that we were rarely ill, merely that she was over-protective and nervously anticipating events, so zealous of our well-being that the mildest of wheezes was seen as incipient pneumonia. While my father, my brother and I were robustly healthy, my mother was delicate. More correctly, she believed herself to be delicate because she had been brought up to think that she was. This conviction led her to frequently hand us over to Annie's care as she retired to bed during the day with some unspecified condition, not serious enough to require a doctor's attention, but necessitating long hours of solitude, possibly with a stack of recent novels on her bedside table.

Bowls of jelly derived from carageen moss, a type of seaweed, were among her patent nostrums. This had the unpleasant glaucous colour and the texture of stinging jellyfish and was recommended as a cure-all. It required endless persuasion to convince me that it was not actually boiled jellyfish. However, of all her witch's brews, cabbage-water was the most noxious and repellent. Allegedly guaranteed to clear the skin, a remedy hardly required by boys who were a long way from being teenagers afflicted with acne and other skin blemishes, the cabbage-water became the bane of my life. This liquid was a constant presence and, since I have no recollection of ever eating cabbage with meals, it must have been purchased solely in order to produce this appalling potion— pale green and smelling of urine. Because no adult was ever seen to consume the cabbage-water, it seemed manifestly unfair to expect that I should willingly do so and its appearance was guaranteed to produce a protracted struggle until I succumbed. Which was preferable: to forego dinner if the cabbage-water had been refused, or to consume cabbage-water before dinner? In the first option you starved, in the latter you felt nauseous for hours.

If most of my mother's medical theories were of a prophylactic nature, when she herself experienced a twinge, she was in bed for the day, or a week if it seemed necessary. Annie was obliged to take over running the household and preparing the meals unsupervised. Her culinary skills were not well-developed and, while she was able to follow the daily routines dictated by my mother, without supervision, no meal ever emerged as intended. Whether it was that she just was not good at making the connection between related ingredients, or she just acted on impulse, giving no thought to what she was doing, the result was the same.

Promptly following my father's arrival home each day, we sat down to eat our evening meal. The table had already been prepared. With my mother absent from the kitchen, the trains still ran on time, but frequently the goods wagons was empty, or the incorrect freight was being conveyed. My father's response to the day Annie put the apples in the stew and the onions in the pie was not favourable. Having already remarked that the stew was unduly sweet, he knew the reason when the hot apple pie and cream was served for dessert. Careful presentation of a meal my mother always regarded as a prerequisite, and the visual effect was given due consideration: the pastry of Annie's pie was beautifully glazed and crimped, and with barley-sugar braiding on the rim, the very image of advanced baking skills. The smell was slightly tangy, but the taste was of baked onions! Annie was summoned and ordered to remove the offending pie from the table, and my mother was encouraged to resume her duties. The garrison needed to eat.

CHAPTER 23

Mary Mary took time to establish herself in my interest. She did not make jokes, rarely laughed and was in awe of Grandmother, of my mother and Mrs Luby. Having been the recipient of a few of the aunt's sarcastic observations on her dusting skills, or her lack of finesse at polishing the fire-brasses, the occasional visits of the aunt struck Mary Mary with acute verbal paralysis. This lasted until the departure of her tormentor.

I was on Mary Mary's level as an innocent and she regarded me as a confidant in her devotions, instructing me about the strange lives and painful demises of her cultic figures. While I had enjoyed Mary Brigid's cinema stories, I was equally interested in Mary Mary's tales, although I regretted that they were not accompanied by theme songs. Within weeks of her arrival, I had a wide knowledge of the cruel practices of torturers and sadists who were determined to extract recantations from scores of saintly virgins and young men of unblemished character. Mrs Luby expressed her disapproval by sniffing determinedly when saints and martyrs were mentioned at the kitchen table, but soon became involved in the topic. She contributed some grisly martyr anecdotes of her own to Mary Mary's wide knowledge of these matters. One evening as my father was walking me home, I shared with him my new-found expertise in hagiography. To my surprise, he was not just unimpressed, but hostile.

'The child's head is being filled with mumbo-jumbo by that cretinous maid in your mother's house' was his comment when we arrived home. 'That new maid may have to go. A bit thick, and does not seem overly energetic. You may have to have a word with Mrs Luby.'

The sheer scale of Mary Mary's religious imagination was only beginning to become evident to me and I remained silent about it in the future: I never mentioned the candles.

At first Mary Mary had placed some small religious picture with an attendant night-light on the kitchen mantelpiece. My mother observed this manifestation with displeasure. 'I think, Mrs Luby, that my mother would not approve of such displays' served as a warning to the housekeeper to keep her underling in line, followed a few days later by a more definite order: 'Religious emblems are not, what shall I say, appropriate to this house. Do you understand me fully, Mrs Luby? See that they are removed.'

The housekeeper, irritated by the fact that she had failed to curb the new maid's ostentatious devotions, and was now being accused of maintaining the same sentiments, replied with a meek 'Yes,'m, of course,'m. Quite right,'m. I never thought to offend,'m', and removed the tawdry and sentimental icons. Later, she told the maid to confine her religious activities to her room and her free time. From this rebuke, the great work of a domestic Sistine Chapel at Rosenheim evolved.

Initially, Mary Mary merely colonised the dressing table with candles in saucers and small bottles, arranged in front of saintly images. Then she noticed that the appearance of the reflection in the mirrors doubled this effect and was picked up by the wardrobe and the glass of the framed pictures on the walls. After Mrs Luby had gone home, Mary Mary moved mirrors from the unoccupied rooms and set them in corners. Then in front of each mirror she made a separate shrine until there was only floor space to pass perilously between the displays. Like a chapel sacristan, Mary Mary was all day engaged, when unobserved, in keeping the candles replaced and tending the work of art she had created.

When Grandmother was awake, Mary Mary was rather more attentive to her needs than her romancing predecessor. It seemed to my mother that the issue of Grandmother's care had been satisfactorily resolved. Mrs Luby busied herself in the kitchen, polishing silver and brassware and repairing household artefacts in order to ready them for sale. Since all these items came from the unused bedrooms or cupboards about the house, my parents never noticed their gradual depletion.

First the crinoline lady tinkled, then the Dutch Boy rang a basser note, then the push-bell sounded long and sharp: eventually the cane tap-tap-tapped on the floor. Grandmother was awake. We had been sitting in the kitchen, helping Mrs Luby to polish the spoons from a set of silver cutlery when the carillon sounded.

'Mary Mary, you go upstairs and see what the old mistress wants', Mrs Luby commanded. Mary Mary had reluctantly been beating carpets for an hour in the back garden and felt that she needed a rest.

'You go, boy', she said to me plaintively, out of Mrs Luby's earshot. 'See what your gran is ringing for.'

Dutifully, I set off up the stairs at a trot. For a change, Grandmother's bedroom was sunny. Perhaps the brightness had awoken her from the usual state of torpor and perpetual dozing. She was sitting upright as I entered the room, her hair curls cascading down her shoulders. She seemed fully awake.

'Fetch my other walking stick, boy. I am going downstairs to see what those slatternly housemaids are up to, drinking tea and preening themselves in front of the mirror, I don't doubt.'

Startled, I backed out of the room and hopped down to tell the women in the kitchen. Both sprang from their seats and dashed up the stairs, Mary Mary in leaps, Mrs Luby more sedately, but showing an agility previously unsuspected. Grandmother met them on the top landing, a tall and ghostly figure like the first Mrs Rochester, in floor-length white nightgown, a walking stick in each hand.

'I am coming down to inspect. Mrs Luby. Fetch me my dressing gown, my good woman.'

While Mary Mary supported Grandmother, Mrs Luby got her robe and put it over her shoulders. Slowly she descended, pausing step by step. She entered the kitchen and saw the spoons, knives and forks laid out on the table; the silver polish, the shammy cloths. All this looked like clear evidence of diligent domestic industry. Abruptly she turned, the effort of her journey beginning to tell on her.

'That will do, Mrs Luby. I am gratified to see that you are not neglecting your duties. Dedicated application is the key to a well-run household. I will return to my bedroom.'

With enormous difficulty they managed to get her upstairs again, the effort of which seemed to sap her of all strength. She collapsed silently into bed, lay back and closed her eyes.

As I was walking home with my mother, I asked her 'What does "a narrow escape" mean?' I was questioned as to where I had heard the phrase, and related that Mrs Luby had used it after the silver polishing had been resumed, following Grandmother's visit to the kitchen. My mother's only response was a long-drawn-out 'Oh, I see.' Later I overheard her relating what I had said to my father, who replied witheringly 'That devious old trollop was up to something certainly. We should send your sister with her magnifying glass to investigate. She might like to fingerprint the staff!'

When Mary Mary was out of the house on an errand for the housekeeper, I would slip inside her room to gaze in fascination at the candlelit display. In time, curiosity overcame my awe, and I added a night-light or two to the flaming rows. Sometimes I even took a new candle from the boxes, and placed it at one of the shrines. I was interested in the image of a shiny black young man, so much more real to me than the pasty-faced women with popping eyes, the grizzled saints, or the one naked man, peppered with little arrows like my mother's pin cushion. I concentrated on adding to the black saint's display when the custodian of the chapel was out of the house. Mary Mary saw in these unexplained additional votive candles evidence of a miracle. She told the sceptical Mrs Luby that a great work of faith was to be seen in the world, and that candles were lighting spontaneously in her room. Mrs Luby glanced suspiciously over her glasses in my direction, the puce of her cheeks getting a shade darker. She then busied herself with mending an ornamental Staffordshire plate which had been chipped and put in the attic years before. When the maid had resumed her sweeping, Mrs Luby quietly said to me, 'Boy, never, ever, go into that girl's room, nor touch her things. She may be a bit simple, but she is not afraid of work, so we would not wish to lose her. If she left, your ma would be very upset.'

The prospect of Mary Mary vanishing like Mary Brigid and Mary Street made me seriously anxious, as did the more alarming thought of my mother hearing that I had lit candles at the shrines of obscure and doubtless proletarian saints; my secret preference for the young black man would surely have been regarded as controversial.

My daily presence in Rosenheim was ostensibly 'to keep Grandmother company', but also to spy on the housekeeper and the maid. My parents never explicitly voiced this latter commission, but when I returned home each evening I was quizzed about the day's events in the other house. My failure to relate evidence of Mary Street's love life, or her successor's devotions, subsequently led my father to consider me particularly unobservant and self-involved. To my mother, I was merely unaware.

My daily round, after I was delivered to Rosenheim, was to sit and be fed in the kitchen by Mrs Luby, then to inspect the rooms and dark spaces of the house, one by one, in roughly the same order, and lastly to nip into the maid's room and add a candle to one of the altars. Otherwise, I sat in Grandmother's room for hours, played with the radio or read falteringly to her from the *Cork Examiner*— the Deaths column first, then the headlines, followed by a tortuous rendering of what followed in the body of the text if the topic was of interest to her. My reading was slow, and my difficulty with place-names (Limerick being as challenging as Leningrad) such that she often drifted into a doze while I read on. Nonetheless, I kept on reading in order to be in a position to resume the narrative, with less hesitation over long words, when she awoke. If she remained soundly asleep, I escaped, until summoned by bells. Then I tiptoed back to my seat by her bedside and continued. Perhaps she really was interested in what I read out, or was merely just encouraging me to read? She never commented except to urge me to read on.

'What else is on the page, boy?'

'Go on boy, go on. You are so slow.'

When I hesitated too long over a word with more syllables than I could manage, Grandmother dozed off. She never helped me to elucidate a difficult word and probably secretly was amused by my mangling of the language. When, in one of my daily reports at home in Windermere, I announced that I had been reading to Grandmother about the 'con-centrat-ion camps in Ger-many', my mother paled visibly, later remarking to my father that 'The boy may be upsetting Mother'. He was adamant that I was a force for good.

'There is no evidence of that; she enjoys his company and a family presence, even if only of a child, calms her.'

Further revelations from the 'con-centrat-ion camps' followed from my daily readings, to which I also treated Mary Mary and Mrs Luby. The kind-hearted maid greeted my accounts of horrors in Germany, the location of which was as obscure to her as to me, with gasps of distress, while Mrs Luby drew in her breath and remarked, 'Them Huns is a tricky crowd, I don't doubt.'

Mrs Luby continued to pilfer from the house, which was a cornucopia of ornamental objects jammed into cupboards, remnants of Grandfather's collection of porcelain and Japonaiserie. Ethically, she confined her pilfering to items damaged in the past and stored away out of sight on the upper shelves of sculleries. For these items she had discovered a market in the antique trade and, with commendable discretion, had resisted the temptation to remove things of value that were on display. My mother was unlikely to notice, and a further visit downstairs from Mrs Luby's employer was improbable since her last foray had left her in a state of collapse. My father, however infrequent his visits to Rosenheim, always noticed, even if things had been moved from one bureau to another. Besides, he had such a poor opinion of the housekeeper that she was on her guard against giving him grounds for suspicion. She correctly surmised that items unseen were not within even his terms of reference.

CHAPTER 24

There was no love lost between my father and his sister-in-law. The aunt never passed up an opportunity for making dismissive or sarcastic remarks at his expense, generally without the satisfaction of eliciting any firm response from him. World War II was just over, petrol rationing had ended, and the smooth black car had emerged from our garage where it had, for the period of the war (for ever, in my memory), presided, supported on a trestle like a casket in a tomb-chamber. I had never seen the car outside or running on the road, and used to creep into the garage, although I was forbidden to do so, and clamber into the leather-smelling comfort of the driver's seat. Lodged in this comfortable womb, with the doors and windows closed and the garage providing a further layer of sound insulation, the outer world seemed to me very distant. I might hear my mother or Annie calling me, as though miles away, but the voices seemed so faint, on some remote island or speaking from the top of a high tower, that it was easy to feel no urgency to respond.

We had driven to the railway station to collect the aunt, her first visit since the car had been returned to the road. She got off the train, all bustle, impatience, cases and packages, tossing orders to the porters, who were commanded to carry her luggage; we were not allowed even to assist. She glanced at the car and the first thing that caught her eye was a crack in one of the small side wing-mirrors, for which parts were still unavailable.

'Your car, like yourself, is cracked', she said to my father, by way of opening gambit. He gazed silently into the distance as though observing troop movements on the far horizon and remained silent. She got into the passenger seat, but was not to be satisfied until he had showed some signs of annoyance, and continued: 'I am surprised that you could afford such a car, but perhaps it is British Army surplus, used for conveying floozies around the purlieus of Amsterdam. Was it very cheap?'

The car, my father's pride and joy, bought expensively in the late nineteen thirties, had been regularly overhauled throughout the war, its engine tuned, its tires inspected, its body polished. The aunt was now intent on undermining his favourite possession. While this one-sided exchange was taking place, my mother was becoming agitated. Her sister had emerged from the train and, without even getting into the car, had opened hostilities along a broad front, delivering some well-aimed salvos at the enemy positions. It was only a matter of time before my father responded with a counterattack; poison gas or blanket bombing might be expected, even a bayonet charge. I had heard much about trench-warfare at Rosenheim.

The aunt's repertoire of abusive invective knew no bounds and it was her intention to cause as much domestic turmoil as possible. She had for years resented most things about her younger sister, who was gentle, pretty and unassertive. That the aunt had remained single while what she regarded as her not-too-bright sister was happily married, with a handsome husband and family, was a cause of unbounded jealousy and the source of much of her antagonism. Not indeed that she herself had ever had any intention of marrying; she lacked understanding of small children, disapproved of men, and considered sex unnatural. Anything she might do to undermine my mother's equanimity, she would regard as a good day's work. If she managed to unsettle my remarkably tolerant and good-humoured father, so much the better. Idiotic remarks, for which she would have evinced the greatest contempt if they had been uttered by someone else, were quite acceptable if they managed to irritate my father. Her attack on the car was calculated to annoy, and it succeeded.

Halfway between the railway station and Windermere, she returned to the topic of the cracked wing-mirror.

'Yes, I suppose, it means seven years' bad luck', she said with a hearty laugh, 'or', leaning over from the front passenger seat, to smile at the driver, 'perhaps in your case, fourteen.'

She smirked with satisfaction at this barb, adding as an afterthought, 'I see that there is serious rust on the bonnet. Of course there is no craftsmanship at all these days in English cars!'

We had reached the middle of Patrick Street, the city's busy main thoroughfare, jammed with horse-drawn brewery drays, business delivery vehicles, buses, bicycles, pedestrians, women with prams, and a smaller number of private cars. Abruptly, my father braked, bringing traffic behind him to a halt, got out of the driving seat and went to the rear luggage rack from which he unstrapped the aunt's cases and packages and set them down on the street. Then with a display of stage-gallantry, he opened the passenger door with something between a bow and a sneer. She recognized the enemy's superior strategy and stepped out of the car with as much dignity as she could muster, and stood in the midst of the traffic with her cases. My father resumed the driving-seat and drove off with a sharp tooting of the horn, whistling happily to himself. Enemy routed in first engagement, further salvos might be expected.

Although she had intended to stay at Windermere, the aunt was, later in the day, to be found installed at Rosenheim, assuaging her irritation at my father by making life intolerable for Mrs Luby and the maid. After a few days' respite, during which she grew bored with threatening to dismiss them both, and feared that they might actually leave if she harassed them further, she would come to visit us instead. An unspoken truce was declared, with hostilities suspended until she was due to end her visit. Then some opportunity would present itself: she would dismiss my father's judgment of the international political situation, or would deride some new household gadget of which he was proud. Her particular talent was to pour scorn on anything that might imply that her sister's husband was notably competent in practical matters. She preferred to suggest that he was actually a ham-fisted clod. The fact that he had successfully mended the then-revolutionary acquisition of a pop-up toaster, or took the radio apart on the dining room table and reassembled it so that it resumed reception was somehow turned into a defeat.

'Those toasters never last; a complete waste of time. It will break down again irrevocably; they are only made of tin-cans', or 'Once a radio has been repaired, it will never work properly again.'

These fatuous examples of rustic wisdom upset my mother, and drove my father to silent immersion in his latest travel book on Ulan Bator or the siege of Omdurman, ignoring her so successfully that he managed to forget her divisive presence. Having come close to emptying Rosenheim of staff, successfully causing her brother-in-law to refuse to acknowledge her existence, and reducing my mother to tears at the mere thought of a visit from her sister, the aunt departed for home, happy and well-satisfied with her trip, promising to come again soon. For her, a visit that did not result in confrontation would have been a purposeless outing.

On returning to her country town, she ritually sent lavish parcels of presents to my brother and me, ensuring that my mother must write in acknowledgement. Correspondence would resume, no mention being made of the most recent fraught visit. News was exchanged in this manner, my mother writing dutifully of my grandmother's declining health, the children's progress, problems with the maids; the aunt responding with humorous tales of local life, not far removed from the inanities of Somerville and Ross's Flurry Knox. She wrote eloquently on the rackety behaviour of the local gentry, the unreliability of local tradesmen and the concupiscence of the town's shopkeepers. She always concluded with an inventory of the many new hats or coats she had bought, promising my mother the ones she got bored with, even though she knew her sister would never wear them. A fortnight later, an enormous hatbox would arrive in the post, containing six hats, worn once, in colours, styles and materials which my fashionably dressed mother would not have worn, even when gardening.

Again dutifully, my mother wrote thanking her sister for the lavish gift, and gave the hats to the maid, who said that they might suit her mother, but at any rate there was a parish jumble sale coming up the next month. Within a few weeks, further large boxes came by post as the coats were discarded. They went, like the hats, to charitable sources, some making their way at weekends by bus to distant townlands, where the maid's mother began to appear in unaccustomed finery, or, diverted via Rosenheim, they graced the matrons of the buildings.

Ostentatious costume-jewellery followed the hats and the coats, never to be worn; always needing to be got rid of, with the added dread—what should my mother say if her sister on a later visit enquired after the benefactions? But she never asked. At regular intervals throughout the year, the aunt would descend for another visit and, with the avowed intention of annoying my father, change her travel plans as often as possible. To have managed to get him to go twice to the railway station on fool's errands, because she had decided to travel on a later train, could be considered a coup by proxy, the train-drivers delivering the blow in her name.

My father had been in the army since his twenties and possessed immense respect for order; indeed, he could not conceive of a world run any other way than with a reliable timetable. In response to being told that Mussolini made the Italian trains run on time, he would have found it inconceivable that there was any other way that trains might operate. This almost mystical belief in order made for a highly organized home life. It worked because nobody suggested questioning the concept. My mother took it as a given that her husband would arrive home for lunch if he were in Cork, or dinner if he was out of town. Meals were arranged to coincide with this precise timetable. Blitz, gifted with high-frequency aural powers, could recognize the sound of my father's car when it was still half a mile away and would run up and down the back garden, barking ecstatically. Annie would inform my mother of Blitz's John the Baptist-like behaviour as forerunner, so my father's expected arrival received even more precise confirmation by canine intuition, as accurate as any satellite positioning system. Until the car had pulled up at the back gate, Blitz would not cease his demonstration of paranormal hearing.

The orderly nature of my father's universe extended to the disposition of everything in the house. Unlike in Rosenheim, where nothing had ever been thrown out and where there was no shelf or bureau, which might have looked well with a single Sèvres vase upon it, but was encumbered by eighteen assorted pieces of porcelain, every display in Windermere was as balanced as a Morandi still life, a few carefully chosen objects placed with the care of a Zen master. The mantelpiece, over which *The Avenue, Middleharnis* hung, was of mahogany with curving contours and shelves on two levels. On these were placed a pair of Art Deco methers and some Japanese cloisonné vases; that was all. It was so precise that had the urns been required at midnight to become animated in some fairytale, not until the precise stroke of the clock would they have begun to prance about, and afterwards would have been impelled to return exactly to the positions they had left.

Rosenheim represented for my father the fatal flaw in his ordained world, a source of ungovernable anarchy and confusion, of which he disapproved. His understanding of life was based on a military model of responsibility: the commanding officer, the OC, was the source of all initiatives, the officer-corps interpreted commands, and lower ranks carried out orders. Insubordination could lead one to periods of detention without rations (being sent to bed without supper was a junior version of solitary confinement). Applying such a rigid model to the human condition was not always successful. To pursue the analogy, in our house my father occupied the role of officer commanding Windermere; everyone else was his subordinate, my mother a subaltern, the maid an NCO, the children a batch of raw recruits to the platoon, in need of rigorous training.

The affairs of the Rosenheim outpost were a continual source of exasperation, since military discipline failed to run smoothly in that department, despite the frequent issuing of directives. The disastrous combination of disorder at Rosenheim with a visit from the aunt was capable of sending my father into a mood of dark annoyance, as the established order of the universe was being upturned and primordial chaos invited to invade the citadel. His self-discipline was such that he was never rude or even curt with the aunt, vacillating between civility and benign obliviousness, as a response to her aggression.

A week after her departure, a package of expensive toys would arrive. The reciprocal nature of her gifts, relative to the amount of conflict she had caused, was never discussed in my hearing. A few days after she had returned home, we knew that shortly there would be a rat-tat on the knocker and what my brother and I referred to as the 'P seven C' van would be parked outside. The uniformed messenger came with a substantial box wrapped in brown paper and tightly bound with string. We spent days at the upstairs windows, awaiting the expected arrival of the 'P seven C', which sometimes, inexplicably, failed to appear. My mother surmised on these occasions that a package of gifts had indeed been purchased, but that the aunt had decided to send it to some other family instead, as being more worthy, or as a more urgent peace offering.

The explanation for our cryptic name for the parcel department of the Post Office derived from the fact that the service called itself *Post agus Telegraf*, rendered into *P* and *T*, written in the medieval Gaelic script then still used for all communication in Irish, in which the *T* looked like a C, with the 'and' rendered by a Gaelic ampersand resembling a number seven. So reliably did the appeasement gifts arrive that, when the ritual failed, we assumed that there must have been a postal strike or go-slow in the sorting department. At the end of a week of us awaiting the delivery of a parcel, my mother, aware of the disappointment that the non-arrival of any package caused her children, intoned in a melancholy voice a refrain from Tennyson's most dreary of ballads, 'Mariana in the Moated Grange' —' "He cometh not", she said.'

The aunt had not been in town for more than a few hours before she arrived in Windermere, her face gaunt with furious indignation. My mother greeted her with apprehension. Clearly something dreadful had happened at Grandmother's. The aunt outlined the cause for her anger and took it for granted that I was the culprit.

'Somebody', she announced with a baleful expression, 'has been writing on the piano-keys at Rosenheim. The boy has vandalised a valuable musical instrument. I recognized his illiterate scrawl on the keys.'

Annie was sent to bring me before the piano tribunal for trial and summary execution. I arrived looking guilty, having no idea of what I was being accused. The aunt and my mother were sitting side by side on the sofa, the former looking like a hanging judge, the latter whey-faced and sharp-eyed at having been disgraced again by one of her offspring. I assumed that my pilfering from the biscuit-tin had been detected, and was about to be reprimanded for this theft. Without preamble the aunt began: 'What destructive and evil impulse possessed you to write on the piano keys at Rosenheim? Are you not aware that that piano was purchased at great cost by your grandfather at the Cork International Exhibition of 1902 and is irreplaceable? It is a Wertheim!'

She glared at me so fiercely that I backed towards the door, protesting my innocence. Although I had frequently tinkered with the piano-keys, I had never written on them, nor made any attempt to play an actual tune. My mother twisted her handkerchief with embarrassment; the aunt glared.

'Never, never, have I heard of a child destroying a piano in this way, in all my years of experience as a teacher. You—you are quite incorrigible.' She broke off, removing her gimlet gaze from me and addressed my mother in hectoring tones.

'The boy will have to be sent to a reformatory. It is quite obvious that he is a liar and has an utterly depraved character. Neither you nor his father are capable of disciplining him.'

Any attempt on the aunt's behalf to criticize my father caused my mother to become incensed and rally to his defence, a position she found more difficult to adopt where her children were concerned. The topic moved from me to the idea of my father as a lax disciplinarian. This suggestion was without foundation, because he was strict in a perfectly non-aggressive manner, asserting his authority by force of personality alone. No longer the focus of the conversation, I slipped out of the room and hid in the scullery until I heard the front door slam, and the sound of the aunt's retreating feet clip-clopping on the gravel of the garden path. After a tactful pause, I emerged and sidled into the room where my mother had remained seated, looking out the window in an abstracted manner. Eventually she registered my presence and gazed at me sadly, disappointed at a further lapse in behaviour, and irritated that the aunt should find another occasion to be the harbinger of moral self-righteousness. Naturally, my loyalty to Mary Mary had prevented me from saying that she was the actual pianist, and tinkled the ivories when she should have been polishing the front door knocker, so I had to approach the truth obliquely.

'Mrs Luby loves music and often has a song with her friends.' That Mrs Luby had friends and that I should be familiar with them was news to my mother, so she questioned me. I elaborated on Mrs Dalton and Mrs Therbarry singing music hall ditties over their teacups in the kitchen, in the hope that my mother would guess that someone else was the pianist, without my having to say so. Her dedication to detective fiction brought her Miss Marple-like to the correct conclusion.

'And does Mary Mary sing also?'

I nodded.

'And play the piano sometimes?'

I nodded so vociferously that my neck ached. She got the point immediately.

'You might have said so, and spared me that awful scene. I have a migraine now and will be ill tomorrow.'

'But I said that I didn't do it.' She nodded contritely for not have been more supportive, and for having attached any credence to her sister's accusations.

Looking chastened but off the hook, I skipped out of the room and invaded Annie's territory. Always kind and patient, she had heard the raised voices and glanced up apprehensively. She looked at me with sympathy.

'Annie, what is a refor-matory?' She dropped a cup into the sink with an amused grin.

'A school for naughty boys. Run away now and play or you might go there.'

Later in the day the aunt returned in chortling form, unable to suppress a smile of satisfaction. She threw her hat on the dining room table, in an uncharacteristic level of informality.

'I dismissed that slovenly creature Mary Mary, and instructed Mrs Luby to find a replacement specimen by this evening or I would fire her as well.' My mother stared with incredulity.

'You did what?'

'I have cleansed the Augean stables in Mother's house. Those women are a disgrace and it speaks very poorly of your concern for her that you are not revolted by their moral turpitude, which has been leading the boy into delinquency and depravity. You will have to get the piano restored; it will probably be expensive. I must rush now—I am going shopping for some scarves and shoes.'

As abruptly as she had arrived, she departed, this time without slamming the front door, in anticipation of the multicoloured delights of the city's clothes shops.

The focus of attention in 'The case of the inscribed piano keys' had now shifted from myself to another suspect, a below stairs serving-girl from an adjacent hamlet, whose tastes were known to be musical. Miss Marple ruminated on this intelligence and decided that swift action should be taken. The lady detective and her child-assistant set out for Rosenheim, arriving in time to forestall the engaging of a new maid. Mary Mary was reinstated, reprimanded for writing the notes in pencil on the piano-keys and recommended to stick to her duties.

'But, 'm, I meant no harm by it, 'm. I was just trying to learn the latest songs, 'm...' The piano keys were cleansed of the incriminating notations and Mary Mary confined her musical studies to the evenings when she was alone in the house with Grandmother.

The following morning a delivery-man from one of the smarter shops arrived with two large boxes decorated with stripes and ribbons, their purchaser now unseen because she had removed her residence to some more suitable quarter. Without explanation she would reappear in a few days or a week, making no reference to her absence, to the piano, the fired and reinstated maid, or to her false accusation. No apology would be offered. Jollity would be the keynote of her behaviour, witty stories and good fellowship. The latest novels in Miss Finney's lending-library would be recommended to my mother. Even to my father, pleasantries would be addressed, although he was never disposed to acknowledge the aunt's changes of tack, knowing that in every mood-change lurked a potential ambush. Conversely, my mother always hoped for the best, that a change of heart might herald a genuine era of better relations, and an end to domestic warfare.

In Rosenheim, Mary Mary, and in Windermere the aunt, went about the separate houses humming lightheartedly the same wartime song: the aunt slurring over the romantic words while concentrating on the tune, the maid enunciating the lyrics carefully, while wishing for the night-time when she could, without fear of observation, pick out the notes on the piano.

CHAPTER 25

When Grandmother was not reminiscing about the trenches and the 'dear boys', the sinking of the *Lusitania*, the Black and Tans and the burning of the city, she liked to talk of Grandfather, a topic in which my historical ignorance was less likely to cause her anger. In her view, her late husband belonged to that most perverse, yet most-to-be-respected, department of the human species, the male. Her principles were challenging and contradictory to my ears: men had to be approached with an almost reverential respect as the doers and thinkers of the world, the husbands, fathers and sons. But they were, at the same time, fatally flawed, and always prone to absurd whims and the sort of foolishness that undermined their more admirable qualities. This is what she, as his wife, always had to guard against—his amiable and whimsical nature, and occasional fecklessness. Women, though the weaker sex, were infinitely wiser and more balanced. Without their good sense, disasters might occur.

I sat on my perch by the window as she talked, keeping a weather eye on the street, in case something interesting might occur. If Grandmother felt that I was not being attentive, the Crinoline Lady would suddenly sound her tinkling note of rebuke, and I would be drawn back from my reverie. If this failed to detach me from a runaway milk-wagon or altercation between delivery boys on the pavement, further bells sounded. Mrs Luby and Lill in the kitchen would hear the bells and wonder where I could be, since I was supposed to be keeping Grandmother company at that moment. The sound of somebody coming upstairs was followed by Lill's face appearing very low down in the crack of the opened doorway, close to the doorknob. She retreated once she noted that I was in my ordained position. Returning from my scrutiny of the street, I focused on Grandmother's story.

'Your Grandfather was dissatisfied with his earnings at the School of Art, and with his private design and sculptural commissions, so he decided to go into business. I was entirely against it because I felt that he had no commercial experience and would lose money.' The delivery boys' row had developed into a fist-fight outside our gate and I was drawn back to the window. The dinner-bell yelped a harsh 'drinng', and I reapplied myself to her story.

'However, once he had determined on something, it would have been wrong to stand in his way. He toyed with many ideas; of importing tiles or ceramics, or manufacturing his own. He had the skill, although he had never done so on a large scale. These schemes preoccupied him for a while, until he got the idea of something that could be manufactured with ease, and for which there was a ready market.'

The doorbell rang and I sprang to the window, waiting for the door to be answered and to see if someone would come into the house, or go away. After a second ring, Lill emerged from the kitchen and I could hear a conversation taking place at the doorway. I watched the unknown person retreating up the garden path to the gate, before turning into the street. The Dutch Boy gave an insistent throb and I again turned my attention to Grandmother's talk.

'Eventually he came to the solution quite easily. He smoked a meerschaum himself, so he asked the question: why not manufacture pipes, just not so elaborate as the meerschaum?' I had later found this pipe in one of Grandmother's cupboards, resting snugly in its S-shaped box, lined in a faded but originally deep red velvet.

'Clay tobacco pipes for ordinary folk – that's what he decided to manufacture.'

Although I had never been taken there, I recollected conversations overheard, in which 'the factory' had been mentioned, and among the detritus of the house there were possibly hundreds of clay pipes, some scattered on shelves in the bedrooms, others in the bottoms of drawers among the faded coloured paper poppies on their rusty pins, and many in damp cardboard boxes in the garden shed. These pipes felt weightless in your hand and broke easily if you held them too tightly.

'He bought a premises in the city, not far from the School of Art, and set up his factory there. Soon he had a few men working for him and the business was in production. He made the models himself and in time had a range of all sorts of pipes, long and short, suitable for men and women and for different occasions. In no time they were being transported around the country, packed in tea chests with straw. The clay pipes were a success and so, out of nothing, he had conjured a successful business that he could supervise when en route to his teaching. Only when they went out of fashion did the trade drop off, but then he died, so we did not keep up the business.'

At this point it was Grandmother's turn to drop off into a reverie, to be followed by sleep.

When I was sure that she was no longer awake, I departed noiselessly for the kitchen.

When the topic of the clay pipes was resumed, the details and emphasis had altered, as though Grandmother had forgotten the original story, or perhaps this version was the correct one? By gingerly questioning, one might possibly learn more.

'But the men in the factory took to drinking whiskey for breakfast and, since they were unsupervised most of the time, they were drunk for the rest of the day. Then they got into fights and many pipes were broken. The quality of the pipes deteriorated, the stems became crooked and sometimes they had no flue at all in them. Having been sent all the way to a distant customer, a reply would come that they were as solid as stone and completely useless. Your grandfather had neglected this aspect of the matter—that the factory would not run by itself without problems.'

I had seen some of the rejected pipes in the garden shed and remarked that I had done so.

Unfortunately, I had also made the mistake of interjecting and lost the remainder of this much more dramatic version of the tale.

'You shouldn't be prying in to what does not concern you. I shall have to speak to Mrs Luby immediately.'

She reached out, grabbed one of the bells and rang it repeatedly. Further rings evoked no response from below, and in the reverse of the staff coming to see why I was neglecting my duties, I was dispatched to see what they were up to. Oblivious to the bells, Mrs Luby and Lill were sitting at the kitchen table, preoccupied as Mrs Therbarry related some lurid local gossip. Conversation ceased abruptly when I entered the kitchen.

'Grandmother was ringing.'

'We heard. Where were you?' Mrs Luby eyed me.

'Listening to Grandmother talking about the factory and the pipes.'

'Pipes is it? More like corkscrews they were; I seen them myself in the sheds. What does she want?'

'To complain about me.'

Lill galloped up the stairs to enquire, leaving a cloud of dust hanging in the air where she had pounded the stair-carpet.

Lill, the new maid, had replaced Mary Mary in unexplained circumstances. I arrived one day at Rosenheim to find the religious maid gone and her sanctuary cleared of all evidence of cultic practices. She had been replaced by someone half her height. When I asked what had happened to Mary Mary, I was told by Mrs Luby not to be so inquisitive. I assumed that the shrines had been discovered but, as I later learned, a slight deficit in the housekeeping small-change had been the cause. Lill was so short that she was no taller than me. Clearly the bottom of the barrel (or tea-chest) was being reached where staff for Grandmother's house was concerned; if they got any shorter, they might vanish. Lill was what would be known today as a person of short stature, but in the unenlightened, and politically supremely incorrect, late nineteen forties, she was a midget. The roundness of her face gave her a child-like appearance, emphasized by the incongruousness of her hair, worn in short pigtails, a style never seen on adults. Short she may have been, but her energy was prodigious. Where her predecessors carried a single bucket of coal upstairs for the maintenance of Grandmother's fire, Lill, with the muscular arms and build of a Sumo-wrestler, took two buckets at a time, lurching up the stairs at speed on her diminutive legs, with a scatter of coal lumps falling behind her as she went, grinding coal dust into the carpets. Mrs Luby had to restrain these displays of vigour, and enjoined her to carry less coal and to see that it all got to the upstairs coal-scuttle.

While Lill could not be described as a new broom, she contributed an appealing willingness to household tasks. Her energy was such that Mrs Luby had to restrain her wish to polish silver, for fear that she would remove the plating of the inferior pieces with her strenuous buffing. Lill was cheerful and either hummed or sang while at her work, introducing me to a wide repertoire of traditional songs which had not been aired in Windermere – 'It was a lover and his lass' – 'the bright May morning-o'—and sundry refrains echoed around the house as the jolly singer moved about – 'and I lost my maidenhead'— knocking over things and unsettling Mrs Luby's state of mind. When I questioned Lill as to what the words of a particular song meant, I often noticed Mrs Luby gesturing to her to ignore my enquiries.

In her customary manner, my mother had written to the aunt, giving her the current family news, and mentioning Lill as the new arrival in Rosenheim, following Mary Mary's summary dismissal. She made the fatal mistake of mentioning Lill's diminutive stature, a fact that could not have been otherwise suspected. The aunt was intrigued, and to my mother's chagrin, announced an imminent visit. Within a week she had arrived and, ignoring her expected presence at Windermere, established herself at Rosenheim, no doubt the better to engage in an anthropological survey of recently identified midget tribespersons from the buildings, each female warrior equipped with blowsticks, poison darts and coal bucket.

Lill was admirably self-possessed and not disposed to regard any employer with undue awe. The aunt presented no particular difficulty for her, just another overbearing and demanding employer, to be humoured for the sake of holding on to the job. To the aunt, Lill was an ideal fount of fresh anecdotage with which to entertain her friends. Lill was as kind-hearted as she was hard-working, paying more genuine attention to Grandmother, 'a fine lady', than did any of her predecessors. She was happy to read the newspaper out loud for hours, even while Grandmother slept, and to read it again when she awoke. In between such marathon sessions, she scrubbed and cleaned with a light heart, whistling or singing to herself as she toiled. The aunt observed the behaviour of such a model slavey with amusement, and sought means to discomfort her. Dusting in positions too high for her four-feet stature struck the aunt as a novel venture, and she sent Lill to the never-used sittingroom to dust. After a while there was a crash of breaking glass and Lill met the stern-faced aunt at the door of the room, declaring with insouciant aplomb, 'It fell, 'm', as the remains of some treasured Venetian glass vase lay shattered on the floor.

Although the aunt might have dismissed Lill on the spot for breaking a household ornament, she did not do so, in order not to be diverted from her intention to wrong-foot the overly willing maid. The aunt retired to consider other means. Blacking the kitchen range was one of the most disagreeable household chores for any servant, and Mrs Luby performed this nasty job as infrequently as possible. Instead of the approved, jet-black and shiny appearance to be expected of any well-run kitchen, the range looked dull and begrimed with ash. The blacking of it became Lill's next duty, entailing hours spent covering all its parts with liquid blacking, and then polishing the surface when the blacking had dried. It was considered impossible to engage in this job without ending up with a sizeable quantity of blacking on oneself. This horrid coating then proved difficult to remove. Lill whistled away an entire day, laying on the liquid with a small brush, then shammying it with cloths. The result was a gleaming range, looking as though it had been carved from grainless black marble, its vestal virgin standing beside it, clean and neat, and ready for the next commission.

For a week the aunt remained at Rosenheim, attempting to prove the small maid incompetent, dishonest or stupid. She succeeded in none of these, and found Lill more willing than ever to undertake new duties. Even Lill's whistling grated on her, so she commanded that there should be no whistling or singing in the house because 'it disturbed Mother'. Lill complied, still whistling, but silently, mouthing the tunes as she worked, a strategy which the aunt found challenging, but lacked an adequate means of curbing. Gradually it dawned on the aunt that this small, imperturbable girl was not to be daunted by extra work or ridiculous orders, and was incorrigible in her sense of duty and willingness to work. Defeated, the aunt removed to Windermere, issuing veiled threats before saying to my mother: 'That Lill is a most unsuitable person, altogether too willing for a servant. I am sure she is up to something—a thief no doubt. Perhaps it was precipitate to get rid of Mary Mary.'

What machinations followed were not known to me, nor who took the initiative for further changes in Grandmother's regime. Considering that both my parents and the aunt concurred in the need for stability, the undue degree of fluctuation in the personnel reflected their inability to act together, or to anticipate the catastrophes which occurred with alarming regularity. As much to my dismay as to my delight, Lill abruptly disappeared and Mary Mary resumed her role in the household, her reinstatement as mysterious as her earlier departure. When I asked her why she had left (and why she had returned), she ignored my questioning. Over time and by night, her shrines were secretly reinstalled and normality seemed to be assured: the smell of burning wax again hung heavily in the air.

CHAPTER 26

The housekeeper kept the reinstated but cowed Mary Mary, busy throughout the day, bringing coal or meals upstairs and going on errands. Occasionally she was dispatched with a tightly bound package, to be delivered to a shop in town, with warnings of instant dismissal if it were dropped. The maid was reliable, punctual and not inclined to drop things. More important from the housekeeper's perspective, Mary Mary was lacking in curiosity and did not pry.

It was while she was out of the house on such an errand that the fire began. Mr McWilliams, passing on the far side of the street, noticed the flickering light against the window-blind, and came to the door. Mrs Luby mounted the stairs, three steps at a go, and screamed on entering the maid's bedroom, which was engulfed in flames. She retreated, fortunately having the presence of mind to shut the solid timber door, and to send a passing delivery-boy, on his bicycle, for the fire-brigade. It usually took about fifteen minutes for them to get to the suburbs. Mrs Luby was overcome with conflicting emotions; to save Grandmother and me, to save the house, to save her job, to save

189

her stock of soon-to-be-pilfered goods, all of which were threatened by the smoke issuing from under Mary Mary's door. Sagely, Mrs Luby endeavoured to save all together: the old lady and the boy, the house, the job and its lucrative side-line.

To protect her job, there would be a lot of explaining to do, and whatever far-fetched story my mother might accept, my father would not be impressed. Ahead of the fire-brigade, men from the street, at home for their lunch, came with buckets of water from the kitchen and the bathroom on the half-landing, and began to soak the interior of the bedroom. By the time the firemen arrived, water was flowing in a substantial stream down the stairs. Heat and smoke filled the hall, and sounds of crackling timbers became more audible as the fire took hold. When the fire-hoses were turned on, Grandmother, momentarily forgotten, started to ring her bells, just as Mary Mary returned from her outing. Faced with the conflagration, the maid sat down on the front doorstep and wept uncontrollably, her apron over her head. Mrs Luby pushed me into Grandmother's room with the injunction to 'Explain to your gran about the fire. Say it was an electrical fault.' A cloud of dense smoke hung in her room, halfway down from the ceiling. She was sitting erect in bed, looking alarmed.

'I smell smoke, boy. Has that housekeeper been neglecting the range? I am sure something is burning.' I thought it better not to succumb to the temptation of an easy answer and said that a candle had fallen over, and that the fire was out now. She remained unconvinced but asked no further questions, lying back under the dense pall, dozing.

The firemen quickly doused the blaze, which had merely consumed the bedroom furniture and Mary Mary's substantial supply of candle wax. Mary Mary, now seated in the kitchen, had succumbed to hysteria, and the neighbours were attempting to calm her while she shrieked and flailed with her arms. Someone had gone over to Windermere to fetch my mother, who arrived white-faced and terrified at what might have occurred. The soaked hall, now inches deep in water, with lingering smoke clouds, made an unfavourable impression. The damage was surveyed and Grandmother visited, but since she was asleep again, no immediate explanations were required.

Every surface in Mary Mary's room was black and charred, but the door had contained the blaze. The hundreds of candles had melted in the heat, and any evidence of the shrines was likewise consumed. All that could be seen in the room were the blackened skeletons of furniture, charred floorboards and an inexplicable accumulation of burned mirror frames with their shattered glass. From the remains of the mirrors my mother deduced that Mary Mary had been intensely vain, a previously unsuspected character defect. Later, my father arrived, and Mary Mary was sent home with mention of the police being called. Red-eyed and trembling with shame, she left the house, her good name irrevocably damaged her shrines, her clothes and possessions lost to the flames like those of her predecessor. At least, neither her life nor anyone else's had been sacrificed on the ecclesiastical pyre. Mrs Luby was deputized again to remain in the house until Mary Mary's replacement could be found and the bedroom refurbished.

I was questioned about the fire, as was Mrs Luby. Her version made no mention of the thousand-candle-power display in the Holy of Holies, of which she may have been ignorant, having herself rarely gone upstairs. I, unfortunately, described in considerable detail the shrines, the candles, the altars, the little statues, and worse, the interest I had developed in all Mary Mary's passions. My parents listened in disbelief, aghast that that Grandmother's house should have been harbouring such a pyromaniacal and dangerous character. I, as putative carer and companion to Grandmother, was deemed an utter failure.

'First, we have a whore, then an arsonist', my father remarked. 'This was a very narrow escape.' Weeks passed, the maid's room was cleared of debris and restored. Mrs Luby remained in residence, doing reluctant double-duty, to which Grandmother objected, believing that the strict demarcation lines between the duties of maid and housekeeper were being breached. A new maid, preferrably neither overly amorous, not a fire-raising religious extremist, would have to be found.

Mrs Luby, having sold such items as could be removed without their absence being noticed, now turned her attention to the ornaments that were on display. Because the arrangement of the house had not been altered in half a century, the ordained placing of each item of ceramics was sacrosanct. Nothing should, without Grandmother's expressed permission, be moved or even displayed at a different angle from the customary. The closed and untenanted bedrooms might provide further treasures, which in her now unobserved leisure-time after I had gone home, she could adequately explore without my inquisitive questioning or a maid's silent observation. By the time the maids' room was ready for reoccupation, the housekeeper had dispatched a significant collection of objects of vertu from the house, and had every reason to believe that her pilfering would remain undetected.

When she arrived, the new maid was as unexceptional in her habits as her predecessors had been extreme. She had the good fortune—or as a result of my mother's alertness when choosing her—not to be a further Mary, so no adaptation of her name was thought necessary. She was Betty, fat, lazy and uncomplicated. If she could sit all day with Mrs Luby, chatting and having tea and snacks, then she was content. 'A little light housework' was the extent of her work-schedule. She was happy to live-in and minister to Grandmother, now weaker and obviously beginning to fail. My mother acquiesced to a lowering of domestic standards. Grandmother was unaware of even more dust accumulating around the house, the ornamental brasses and fire-irons unpolished beyond a cursory rub.

I observed each successive change of regime with interest, perhaps becoming aware, for the first time, of the range and multiplicity of human society. My own family was composed of immutable presences: myself, my elder brother, our parents, the aunt periodically seen, and Annie, our maid of long standing. Annie had been chosen with the same care as my mother would have devoted to the arrangement of cut-flowers, or the pinning down of a dress pattern. These were constants from which change should not be expected: even Mrs Luby, who had been with Grandmother for years, was a constant in a more non-family-member sense. However the grand progress in Rosenheim, from Mary Brigid through Mary Street and Mary Mary to plain Lill, Mary Mary again and then Betty, was human richness indeed: an extraordinary panorama of real life, undreamt of in Windermere.

These young women introduced me to topics I had never encountered at home, where everything was sedate and ordered. National and international issues were debated in Windermere, books discussed, while in Rosenheim the talk was of young men, saints, and the gossip of the streets. In the more elevated world of my parents, the doings of the neighbours were not discussed, at least not in my presence. In Rosenheim, that the woman in one house at the buildings had no husband but many children, while the woman opposite had two husbands yet no offspring, was brought to my attention. Each house I passed on the way home became a source of continual speculation as to the secret lives of its occupants.

Betty was passive, but with an alert eye to whatever the main chance might be. With me as a now experienced silver-polisher, we weekly cleaned all the items of the silver tea-set, a task which the housekeeper considered to be superior to mere dusting, and was still being maintained under the new and more relaxed dispensation of more tea and less housework; cleaning silver was a sitting-down job. Before long, Betty had become Mrs Luby's partner-in-crime, although the older woman clearly required no assistance. The new recruit egged on the housekeeper, whose more cautious nature had thus far counselled restraint, as the best means of filling her purse, while maintaining her job, which was one with few duties or arduous tasks. 'Keeping an eye on things' was how she presented herself to my mother.

I'll keep an eye on things for you,'m, so that you won't have to worry. I will see that the old lady, the dear soul, is well cared for.'

My mother privately expressed the view that if Mrs Luby had kept a better eye on things, recent events might have been avoided.

When Grandmother rang her bells, Betty laboured up the stairs or sent me to find out what she wanted. Betty was agreeable, soft-voiced, kindly of manner, a diplomat in small ways, although her eye was constantly on the horizon of advantage, even if it was a distant one. Greater opportunity, however, was not to be hers.

From the buildings there were daily visitations to Rosenheim from Betty's young sisters and brothers. They came 'to borrow' items of utility or food, a box of matches or a twist of tea, or asking for 'a few pennies for the shop', if Mrs Luby was in a generous mood. The housekeeper's ample nostrils might have sensed a whiff of deceit from these visits, if she had exercised them. Since she hailed from the same quarter as Betty, she might have made her own enquiries, or indeed was more informed of familial relationships than she acknowledged. However, she seemed oblivious to this development, unless, of course, she was perfectly aware of Betty's status and relationship to the brood of urchins who called to the house. Mrs Luby instructed me never to let them cross the threshold. They always asked for Betty by name: 'Is me big sister Betty in?'

On a day when the nail-eating aunt had come to spend some time with Grandmother, one of the little boys knocked, trailing a few smaller siblings. Startled to find a strange and severely unfriendly face in answer to his knock, he blurted out 'Is me ma in?' The aunt closed the door in his face and went to the kitchen where the plump and smiling Betty was simpering at the table. The aunt confronted her. The brood of children were hers. She was unmarried, and was fired on the spot. No discussion was warranted. As the aunt, with myself running behind, mounted the stairs to alert Grandmother to a renewed domestic crisis, simultaneously the doorbell rang, and another carillon of bells sounded furiously from the top of the house. The aunt paused on the stairs, caught between the demands of the various bell-ringers while Mrs Luby came from the kitchen to attend to the front door. The aunt resumed her progress up the stairs and entered Grandmother's room, with me on her heels. The old woman lay as usual, seeming to be asleep, eyes closed, bell in hand, her face impassively calm. She had just died.

Having ascertained that her mother had indeed passed away quietly, the aunt descended the stairs and entered the kitchen where she addressed the housekeeper in her most commanding of headmistressly tones.

'Mrs Luby', she intoned with a laugh of satisfaction, 'I do not believe that your services will be further required in this house. Please take your things and leave instantly.'

With dignity, Mrs Luby stood up from the table, took her overcoat and shopping-bag and departed, slamming the hall door as she left. As she closed the front gate for the last time, she mused on her dismissal. She had once again been cast out by a tyrannical and suspicious-minded individual. It was indeed good fortune that she had put the remainder of the silver cutlery in her shopping-bag that morning, all polished and carefully wrapped in newspaper. Otherwise the opportunity might have been lost, and it would be more difficult to sell an incomplete set. 'A narrow escape' she said out loud.

Betty, who had been lingering outside the gate with her children since her own ejection, joined Mrs Luby and trailed along behind her, with the children taking up the rear of the procession of outcasts from Rosenheim. Betty was forlorn, bereft; she had not had the presence of mind to put a few trinkets in her own bag, to get things for the children, and had left the house empty-handed.

My mother had been the person ringing the doorbell as the aunt and I had gone upstairs. Now she stood in the kitchen, open-mouthed at the departing procession. Her sister, who was busying herself in the hall, in getting her own hat, coat and handbag, offered no explanation. Returning to the kitchen, she greeted my mother with a curt nod.

'Your mother is dead. I have dismissed Mrs Luby and Betty. I am going out for cigarettes.'

CHAPTER 27

Grandmother lay in state, immobile, apparently asleep, as in much of the time I had spent in her company, except that, like Mary Street, she was now dead, although I did not really believe that this was a condition of finality. At any moment she might awake and begin sounding her bells for attention. However, this could not be, because the bells on the bedside-table had been removed, and were replaced by a pair of tall candles in polished brass candlesticks. With the curtains drawn, these provided the only source of light in the room. I knew for certain that Grandmother was dead when I noticed that the bells were missing. She was dead and it was not considered proper that I should sit alone in her room. My mother, her brother, their spouses or the aunt and various relatives who had a talent for appearing only at deathbeds, as though summoned back across the Styx or from some nether region to mourn, took turns sitting with the deceased, in the days before the funeral, which would leave directly from the house.

Now that fate had arranged for the aunt to be the one who was present at Grandmother's death, it gave her an entirely bogus ascendancy, which she was determined to exploit. No arrangement for the funeral or any other detail of the necessary mourning was to her satisfaction and had repeatedly to be remade according to her own strict ideas of decorum. When the funeral occurred, it was an event of surpassing gloom, not on account of the death, long-expected, of an elderly woman who had not been seen in public for some years, but because the aunt had decided that it should be as melancholy as possible. It should be a dirge to visibly express her own great loss.

Mrs Luby was called back from the buildings by my mother, and reinstated, since refreshments were required for visitors and mourners. She resumed her position in the kitchen, pouring tea and gossiping in equal measure with the new faces, for as long as the aunt was not within earshot. On going into Grandmother's room, the aunt observed that pennies had been placed on the corpse's eyelids. She immediately came downstairs and harangued my mother for daring to indulge in such a pagan and disrespectful custom. My mother protested her innocence, so the aunt's predatory gaze fell on Mrs Luby. She was fired for a second time within days, for good on this occasion. She had, by an unfortunate slip moved into the forbidden ground of popular religious practice, committed the ultimate social blunder and so deprived herself of the pleasure of presiding at the obsequies. Her own estimate of her role as significant mourner would not have corresponded to the sentiments of the bereaved family.

In the confusion of our protracted absences from Windermere because of Grandmother's death, Blitz was forgotten, and exactly when he disappeared went unnoticed. One day he was there as usual, barking at postmen and similar statutory doggy functions, and then he was missing, possibly having again taken up residence with Mr Cotter. Eventually a neighbour came to the door to report a sighting on the wasteland which bordered the ornamental lake at the bottom of the street. Annie, sent to investigate, returned in some distress and my father departed with her in the car. They returned with Blitz, shaking miserably and evidently half-dead. He had probably been hit by a car or truck and had been lying injured for some days. Back in his kennel, he went to sleep and did not awake. The following morning my father loaded his stiff body into the car, announcing that he would never have another dog. Afterwards, he did not so much as mentioned Blitz's name: he was not replaced.

To my brother and me, observing from the upstairs windows, the horse-drawn funeral carriages had a story-book quality, although horse-vehicles were still quite common in the streets of the city. The aunt, determined to mine every ounce of public grief which it was possible to extract from the event, had engaged the most lugubrious of undertaking firms to conduct the funeral. A procession of black, horse-drawn funeral carriages, flanked by walking, Dracula-like undertaker's mutes in silk toppers, their dark suits draped in shiny black sashes, were assembled along the pavement. The paired black horses with black plumes on their heads were ready to convey the chief mourners to the graveside in the cemetery about a mile away. The carriages would be followed by walking mourners, the yet-mobile amongst the shell-shocked, and lastly, mourners in a procession of cars. My brother and I were to be left behind in Rosenheim in the care of some adult. Children, it seems, needed to be spared the displays of profound grief which were to be expected at the graveside. If these took place, they were never subsequently mentioned in my hearing.

The severing of the connection with Rosenheim deprived my life of a great deal of interest. The dramas performed on its stage far outshone the domestic calm that pervaded my own house, and gave the home of an elderly dying woman a sense of heightened theatre. The fact that in Grandmother's house, crime and punishment were enacted, although separately and not reciprocally related, I understood only partially. The murder of Mary Street by a jealous lover had become part of the folklore of the house and locality: each successive maid had been told the story in hushed tones. Mrs Luby luxuriated in the squalour of the shameful behaviour and shocking end of one who refused to listen to authority. The housekeeper's continual larceny, and doubtless that of others employed in the house, was not detected until considerably later, when it was impossible for the goods to be pursued or charges laid. Mrs Luby, an unconscious anarchist, was merely altering the balance of power in society, taking from the haves in order to benefit the have-nots. She would have been an adept of the 'all ownership is theft' dictum, had she encountered it. She relieved her employer of surplus material wealth, in exchange for services rendered and in lieu of an adequate salary. It was an equitable transfer on all sides; she was merely redressing the status quo of the middle-class jackboot which habitually rested on the necks of the denizens of the buildings. Grandmother died without ever realizing the domestic maelstrom in which she had lived; peacefully tolling her bells, remembering the sacrifice of the Somme and Gallipoli, only half-aware of the renewed devastation taking place in Europe during her last years. She would have thoroughly approved of the sombre cavalcade that left her house, trotting slowly to the graveyard, its symbols of high Victorian public mourning and funereal pomp announcing the passing of a *grande dame*.

At some point in her early life, the aunt's energetic and aggressive outlets became internalized, and found their release in the pillorying of her parents, and later of her sister's family. She evidently derived some satisfaction from abusing and intimidating those in whom she detected evidence of weakness. She became, in fact, a domestic bully, trading on the knowledge that her family would not reject her. Whatever she did or said, it would be forgiven in the interests of family cohesion. Unlike my mother or Grandmother, she never spoke well of her father and, if I had the temerity to repeat something that Grandmother had said about him, or asked about some object of his which I had seen in Rosenheim, she would laugh sardonically and say 'the old fool', or something similarly dismissive, hardly calculated to encourage my questioning. His elder daughter did not share in the adulation in which both my mother and grandmother held him. A gentle man, he (in mirror-image of my mother's baffled response to her male children) may not have been prepared for the abrasive nature of his elder daughter, a child Amazon, unafraid of any physical perils, determined to challenge his ordained authority as the revered patriarch of the household. She challenged him at every opportunity.

Grandfather's ancestor-worship was on an oriental level of reverence and pride, and he was fond of expanding on his relations and forebears with tedious repetition. The family of the eighteenth-century lawyer and politician John Philpot Curran stood at the centre of this esteemed family connection which brought in Curran's daughter Sarah, the distraught sixteen-year-old lover of the doomed revolutionary Robert Emmet and, by a remove, Emmet's maidservant, the heroic Anne Devlin, imprisoned and tortured in Kilmainham Gaol in Dublin. Grandfather might have been less keen to claim as a family connection the maid serving at his own table, whatever privations she was prepared to suffer on his behalf. Thomas Moore, on account of his popular ballads commemorating both Emmet and Sarah Curran, were also included in his pantheon, and provided an extended topic on which he could wax lengthy at mealtimes. Grandmother's song-repertoire, in which Moore's *Irish Melodies* formed the core, also paid homage to the same dynasty. But Grandfather's elder daughter (the aunt in embryo), was determined at some point that she had heard quite enough of the whole historic clan of Currans, Emmet and all, with their sentimental songs. One day, bringing a metal saucepan to the table, she concealed it under the tablecloth until the offending topic was mentioned, and then brandished it when her father got into his ancestor-worshipping stride.

'I'll hear no more of John *Enamelpot* Curran!', she screamed, and like the deranged Oskar in *The Tin Drum*, pounded vigorously on the bottom of the saucepan with a wooden spoon, rattling off a tattoo of discordant sounds.

'Enamelpot, tinpot, Philpot, jampot, crackpot', she shouted, pounding on the enamel surface until the room rang with the beating. Grandfather, offended at such a display of disrespect for his revered ancestors (as well as for himself) demanded an apology. She refused to give one and continued her drumming until he left the room. The incident was overlooked until the next time he mentioned the Currans at the table and she repeated her earlier heavy-metal performance. Further offence was taken, and Grandfather refused to be mollified by his wife's entreaties to their daughter to apologize, or to leave the room, so he left the table, acknowledging the defeat of both himself and his forebears, by a saucepan-thumping teenager. The row was not resolved, and they were barely on speaking term for lengthy periods.

In the late nineteen nineties when the aunt was on the point of death (she died the following day), she brought up the subject of her father's papers, something which she and I as adults had never discussed, or even referred to. She was then in her nineties, older than Grandmother had been when she died. The aunt said to me in a voice which she seemed to be summoning from the depths of her person, 'I know that I should never have done it, burning his papers, but what did I know then? I was young, a girl, quite ignorant, not yet twenty years old. What did I know?'

That was all she said and I could not think of anything appropriate with which to respond. For someone as educated and assertive of her intellectual capacity to imply that at any point of her life she had been ignorant and careless was a unique admission of frailty. Throughout my adult life, my mother had repeatedly rehearsed the events of the day of the funeral, and for many years would descend into an impenetrable depression if she brooded on what had been done and how calculated it must have been.

In fact, at the time of Grandmother's death, the aunt was not, as she implied, under twenty, but forty-four, a mature woman, vice-principal of a school, with a formidable intellect and serious educational ambitions as a nurturer of young talent. What motivated her had no doubt being festering since she was 'under twenty', and indeed, in the year that her father died she was twenty years old. On some emotional level she remained paralysed at that point of loss, unwilling to grieve, unable to forgive. Burning almost the entire corpus of her father's art was her supreme act of revenge. The aunt's anger was contained beneath her steely exterior, but her determination to exact the maximum retribution on her parents, her siblings and their spouses remained a lifetime cause.

What she planned to do had the merit of being unanticipated until it had been accomplished. Then nothing could be reversed. Her brother and sister could wallow in their own discomfort; she would go home, satisfied, appeased and justified, smugly relishing her victory over those who had failed to appreciate her own merits and sacrifices.

Her intention was simple: to destroy what should have been respected – the records of her father's artistic career. She would burn all his papers, his drawings and designs, his watercolours, his sketchpads, his diaries: she would destroy everything. Always at her best when a difficult decision had been made, she was ready to begin her task.

As the mourners prepared to leave for the funeral and the horse-drawn vehicles were already lined up at the kerb, she announced that she was too moved by her mother's death and would not be attending the funeral. She would not suffer the meaningless condolences of remote acquaintances, 'pious and well-meaning fools'. No, she would remain in the house and do some necessary tidying. Since she was a continual source of domestic friction, no one attempted to persuade her to joint the cortege: she had a free hand to attend to her plans. In fact, her absence from the funeral came as a matter of relief, since she would have criticized what the mourners were wearing, the behaviour of the undertakers, the inappropriate excremental manners of the horses, the uncouthness of the gravediggers, the coffin; even the demeanour of the corpse itself if that were not a step too far. After the cortege had departed and in what looked like an improbable relaxation of the rules, she sent my brother and me, first to one local shop, and then another on spurious shopping-errands, occupying us until her project was safely underway.

With a display of concentrated energy, she methodically stripped each room of its papers, the portfolios of drawings, the notebooks of sketches, the mysterious wallpaper-like rolls of life-size cartoons for public monuments, copies of art magazines from a period of thirty or forty years before. All the ephemera that had lain undisturbed and accumulating dust since Grandfather's death and possibly for many years before, was conveyed to the back garden and placed on a small open area of grass. Years of neglect and abandonment had allowed the trees and hedges that surrounded the garden to overcome it, and the open space was barely sufficient. When she had accumulated a sufficient pile to create a decent bonfire, she lit it and surveyed her work. As soon as a good blaze had got going, she returned to the upstairs rooms, opened drawers, cupboards, looked along the high-level shelves, until she had further loads to carry out to the bonfire. It took less time than she had anticipated to create the maximum destruction, although the effort of carrying large piles of journals down the stairs and then outside was beginning to tire her. In the midst of her efforts, she experienced a moment of curiosity concerning the armfuls of artwork and correspondence that she was transporting to the blaze, but resisted the temptation. She recognized that any distraction was potentially fatal to her grand intention. She also avoided the possibility of involving us in her fire-raising, knowing that it would have compromised the single-minded nature of her action. This had to be solely her own initiative, a *fait accompli* by the time the mourners returned from the graveyard. So what did she burn? It is impossible to tell, yet there are clues in the abundance which I recollect, although that can hardly be regarded as reliable evidence.

There is a parallel in the manner of the Malahide Papers, Boswell's drafts for the *Life of Johnson* and the journals of his travels which were transferred in a cabinet from the Boswell family home at Auchinleck in Scotland to Malahide Castle in Ireland. The documents were discovered in the nineteen twenties, still in the cabinet, or being used in the house as wrapping paper. In the nineteen fifties, fragments of Grandfather's papers travelled out of Rosenheim to my uncle's house in Kerry in the drawers of a piece of Arts and Crafts furniture, and remained there, undisturbed for a further fifty years. The aunt in her clearing had not been as exhaustive as she intended and this small cache of papers escaped her book-burning zeal. It does not amount to much: a handful of Grandfather's Pre-Raphaelite-influenced watercolours, some early sketchpads from London, a Paris diary, correspondence, juvenilia, some books, a folder of studio photographs of late work. That is all. No Malahide treasure, but the scraps that escaped the pyre confirm the outrage of what was perpetrated.

The fire smouldered for days afterwards until rain turned the remains into a nasty pile of sodden charred fragments and the sooty residue of incinerated papers. When we got back to the house from the umpteenth shopping trip (bribed by the unaccustomed offer of pennies), the mourners were just arriving back from the graveyard. The aunt was sitting with her hat on at Mrs Luby's chair in the kitchen, the teapot steaming, sipping a cup of tea in a satisfied manner. I ran into the back garden to look at the large bonfire shooting its flames into the sky and came back into the kitchen and asked what was burning and why. With a wink, she intoned: 'Little Polly Flinders sat among the cinders, warming her pretty little toes…', adding with a sepulchral titter; 'Oh, just old papers. A life in cinders.'

CHAPTER 28

The metronome of our lives was the routine of the army, my father coming and going with easy regularity, broken only by the occasional duties somewhere else in the country. He left in the morning, came home for lunch or in the afternoon, Blitz barking to herald his imminent return. This was the accepted order.

It was not my father's habit to discuss with my mother his professional options or such deeper feelings he may have had regarding his career. His world was one in which men made decisions, women rallied loyally to their support—the captains and their queens.

A few years after World War II had shuddered to its bloody conclusion, and the child spy, Karl Weber, had returned to Berlin, my father came home one day and announced to my astonished mother, as casually as though he were referring to the weather, that he had resigned his army commission—the decision already taken and irreversible. The rationale for this dramatic change of direction was because promotion was slow for senior officers, and his superiors (there was to be no promotion on merit in peacetime) were still

205

too young to be dislodged by ambitious officers of his rank. He resigned his lifetime career without giving my mother any warning, or feeling disposed to even discuss the matter with her. The stability of their world was undermined by what appeared to be an arbitrary act, uncharacteristic in one who never behaved in an unpredictable manner: her unquestioning loyalty was shaken by his decision, and she regarded his failure to inform her or discuss the matter with her as a breach of trust.

The lure of industry to a man who knew nothing of it seemed a perilous path to pursue, but he followed his former commanding-officer into commerce and, in leaving the army, cut himself off from the stable world he had known, and in which he had felt secure. One week he was going and coming from the barracks on a hill above the city, as he had always done, the next he was living away from home, sitting in an administrative office of a major industrial complex, awaiting the building of a new house for his family. This transition went on for a further two years and proved equally unsatisfactory for both my parents. The dignified world of the army was substituted for the competitiveness of industry, a nascent corporate culture, less respectful of human dignity than the officer corps. Although my father's new work was a mere twenty miles from Cork, his departure to live there during the week, returning only at weekends to Windermere, coincided with the decline of the other focus of my childhood, Grandmother's life at Rosenheim.

He took lodgings in a street in the town where the business was located, from which he returned every Friday night to Windermere. His landlady, Mrs Dotey, ran a boarding house for unmarried men, fed them and mothered them. She regarded her lodgers as overgrown children. Each weekend he came back bearing a gift, not from himself but from Mrs Dotey. This gift was always the same: a substantial basket of fruit, provided by his landlady to sustain him on the immensity of his journey home; apples, pears, oranges and bananas. The basket of fruit became a symbol of my father's defection to another world. I looked forward to the arrival of the fruit basket more than its bearer, and for the almost two years of his journeying back and forth, and before our new house was completed and we eventually joined him, the basket of fruit, placed every Friday evening on the dining-room sideboard, took on the form of a substitute father-figure. It obviously never occurred to my father that a raffia container for fruit had subsumed him, but he had in some sense evaporated from the domestic scene. Mrs Dotey, the progenitor of the raffia proxy parent, was in life a Mrs O'Brien, but had been renamed by my mother on discovering that the good landlady referred to all her male tenants as 'dote' or 'dotey': 'Yes, dotey, you will need some fruit for your long journey home, dotey' was her weekly refrain. Her kindly and mothering presence did not encourage refusal.

The building of the new house took on the aura of a mythical activity. For lengthy periods nothing happened, and it ceased even to be discussed. In the manner of builders everywhere, the workers periodically disappeared for more lucrative or urgent tasks. Then, suddenly the house was ready. A haulage company arrived with immense and cavernous furniture-vans and we departed.

In a brief period of years, the twin pillars of my childhood, Rosenheim and Windermere, were abandoned, and, with them all their familiar associations were jettisoned. Between the tinkling of bells, I could hear Grandmother's frail and hectoring voice declaiming in the shadowy penumbra of her room, 'Wasn't I right, boy, wasn't I right? I said that it would all end badly!'

ACKNOWLEDGEMENTS

All photographs Commandant Stephen Lalor unless otherwise stated.
Images 9, 10, 18, 23, unidentified photographers.
Images 16, 17, courtesy of Crawford Art Gallery, Cork.
Images 13, 14, 24-33, M.J. McNamara papers.
Image 15, Brian Lalor.